Contents

Contents

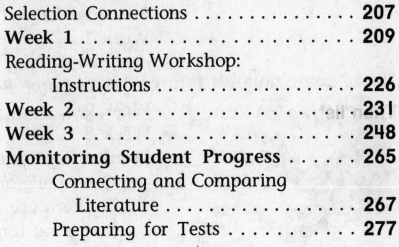

Punchouts

Name _____

Amazing Animals

Name some animals that you think are amazing.

Then list words that describe these animals.

Animal	Describing Words
_____	_____
_____	_____
_____	_____

Write a description that tells about your favorite amazing animal.

Use one of your describing words in the title.

_____

_____

_____

_____

_____

_____

Name _____

Amazing Animals

Fill in the chart as you read the stories.

	What animals appear in this theme?	What amazing things do these animals do?
Officer Buckle and Gloria		
Ant		
The Great Ball Game		

Name _____

Missing Letters

Finish each sentence by choosing a letter or letters from each of the stars below. Print those letters on the line to make a word that makes sense in the sentence.

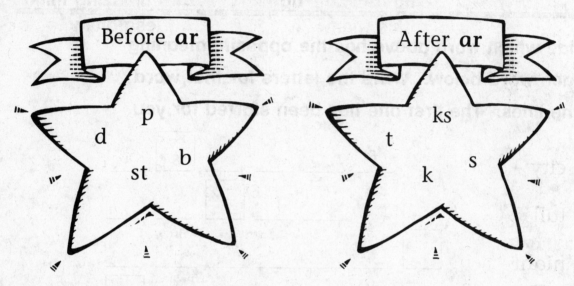

1. Gloria likes to run in the _____ar_____.

2. Gloria _____ar_____ every time she
   sees another dog.

3. Gloria does her _____ar_____ to
   teach safety tips.

4. When the children _____ar_____ to laugh,
   Gloria is happy.

5. Gloria is not afraid of the _____ar_____
   even when she is all alone.

6. Gloria is one of the _____ar_____ at school.

Name _____

Opposites Match

Word Bank

short   more   forget   morning   before   forest   order

**Decide which word above has the opposite meaning
of each word below. Write the letters for that word
on the lines. The first one has been started for you.**

1. city   f __ __ __ [s] t

2. tall   __ __ [ ] __ __

3. night   [ ] __ __ __ __ __

4. after   __ __ __ __ __ [ ]

5. mess   __ __ __ [ ] __ __

6. less   __ __ [ ] __ __

7. remember __ __ __ [ ] __ __

**In the boxes below, write the letters from the boxes
above. The words you make will answer the question.**

8. What did Officer Buckle say when he saw
   Gloria on TV?

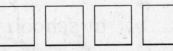 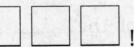

"That's [ ] [ ] [ ] [ ] [ ] [ ] [ ] !"

Name _____

Listen to the Tips

Finish each sentence with a word from the box.

You will use each word twice.

Word Bank

board	listen	told

1. Officer Buckle _____ the students about safety.

2. He asked them to _____ carefully.

3. They paid attention to everything he

   _____ them.

4. He wrote every safety tip on the _____.

5. He told them, "Always remember to _____ to your parents!"

6. When he was finished, some students wrote

   their own safety tips on the _____.

Do not chew gum in school.

Say nice things to your big brother.

Watch your step getting on the bus.

Theme 4: **Amazing Animals**   5

Name _____

Safety Officer Words

Meanings

a. a group of people who watch and listen

b. a person who helps others follow the law

c. something you don't want to happen

d. freedom from danger

e. looking and listening with care

f. orders

Write the meaning from the box to match each word below.

1. accident _____

_____

2. attention _____

_____

3. audience _____

_____

4. commands _____

5. officer _____

_____

6. safety _____

Name _____

Pronoun Show

► A **noun** names a person, a place, or a thing.
► A **pronoun** is a word that can take the place of a noun.

Rewrite each sentence. Replace the word or words in dark print with the pronouns *she, he, it,* **or** *they.*

1. **Gloria** likes to go to school.

_____

2. The **children** cheer when Gloria arrives.

_____

3. You can hear **the cheer** outside the school.

_____

4. When **Officer Buckle** starts to talk, the children are quiet.

_____

5. **Officer Buckle and Gloria** put on a great show.

_____

Name _____

Plan Ahead!

Plan a fun event. Use the form below to help you plan what you will write on an invitation.

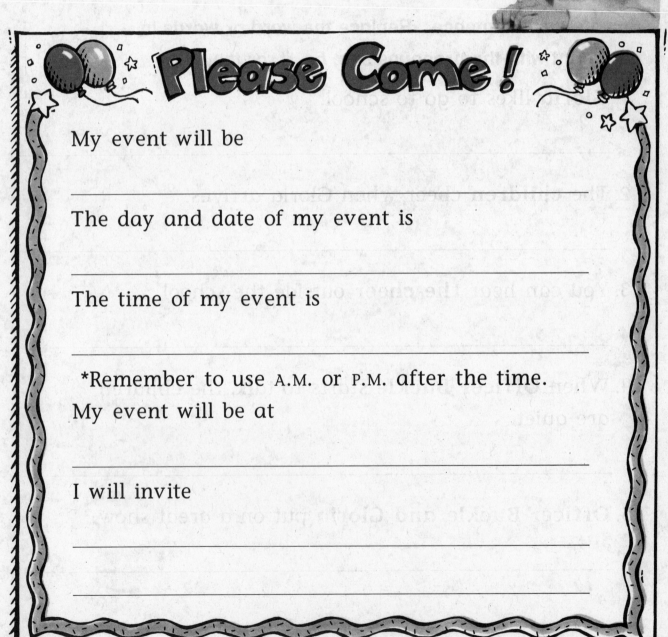

Please Come!

My event will be

_____

The day and date of my event is

_____

The time of my event is

_____

 *Remember to use A.M. or P.M. after the time.
My event will be at

_____

I will invite

_____

_____

Name _____

Check It Out

Each sentence has more than one ending. Read each ending. Put a ✔ next to the ending that tells what happened in the story.

1. When Officer Buckle gave his talks about safety,

   _____ children fell asleep.

   _____ everyone cheered.

2. The principal of Napville School wasn't listening when Officer Buckle said,

   _____ "Always stick with your buddy."

   _____ "Never stand on a swivel chair."

3. While watching television, Officer Buckle saw that

   _____ Gloria sat very still.

   _____ Gloria was the star.

4. Students loved Officer Buckle and Gloria

   _____ because they were a good team.

   _____ they told funny jokes.

Name _____

Drawing Conclusions

Read the story below. Then complete the chart on page 13.

Iguana Fun

Mrs. Persky's class was studying reptiles. So Ada's father brought his pet iguana Boris to school. When Ada's father walked into the classroom, Pedro ran to the back of the room. He stayed there the whole time.

Ada introduced her father and Boris to the class. Boris was dark green and had yellow eyes. Her father took Boris out of his cage. That made Evelyn hide under her desk. Ada said Boris was a nice iguana, but Evelyn would not move.

Ada's father said that Boris was almost fourteen inches long. He explained that this kind of iguana never gets longer than fourteen inches. Ada's father told the children not to worry about Boris. He said that iguanas move slowly after they have eaten. The children counted five orange rinds in the cage.

Mrs. Persky asked if she could hold Boris. Boris wrapped himself around her shoulders. Mrs. Persky talked softly to Boris. Some of the children petted Boris. Everyone thanked Ada's father for coming, except Pedro and Evelyn, that is.

Where Does It Belong?

**Look at these dictionary entries. Write each entry word
on the page where it belongs.**

fail v. : not to succeed
bulldozer n. : a tractor with a blade in front
false adj. : not true
fade v. : to lose brightness or loudness
buddy n. : a good friend
bubble n. : a thin globe of air or gas
falcon n : a bird of prey
browse v. : to look for

brick / buck

_____

_____

face / fair

_____

_____

bucket / bully

_____

_____

fake / fame

_____

_____

Amazing Dog

Use words from the box to finish the sentences about Gloria.

Word Bank

capture	picture	attention	caption
action	station	mixture	motion

1. Gloria is fun to watch when she's in _____.

2. She is a _____ of hard work and fun.

3. Gloria is always ready for _____.

4. Once she helped Officer Buckle _____ a robber.

5. The next day there was a _____ of her in the paper.

6. The _____ under the picture said that she was a brave dog.

7. Everyone at the police _____ loves Gloria.

8. Even the other dogs pay _____ to Gloria.

Name _____

What Time Is It?

Read the paragraph below that tells what a day for a police officer and his dog, Spike, might be like. Then write the times that they did each thing in the schedule below. Remember to include A.M. or P.M. after the time.

At eight o'clock in the morning, the two go for a walk. At nine o'clock in the morning, they drive to Woodview Elementary School. They finish their safety talk at eleven o'clock. At twelve o'clock they stop in the park for lunch. Spike finds other dogs to play with. At one-thirty in the afternoon, they go to Smith Elementary School. Then at three o'clock they help children get safely on the school bus.

Schedule

_____ Go for walk

_____ Go to Woodview Elementary School

_____ Finish safety talk

_____ Lunch in park

_____ Go to Smith Elementary School

_____ Help children get on school bus

Name _____

Pronoun News

Read the article from the school newspaper. Find places where a noun can be replaced with a pronoun. Draw a circle around the nouns that can be replaced.

Today Officer Buckle and Gloria came to our school. Officer Buckle is a safety officer and Gloria is a dog. Officer Buckle gave a safety talk. The safety talk was an important lesson for children. While Officer Buckle was talking, Gloria acted out the tips. Gloria is the funniest dog the students have ever seen. Don't miss their next visit!

Rewrite the article. Replace each noun you drew a circle around with a pronoun. Then read the article you have written to see if it makes sense.

_____

_____

_____

_____

Name _____

Revising Your Research Report

Decide how to make your paper better. Put a check beside the sentences that describe your research report.

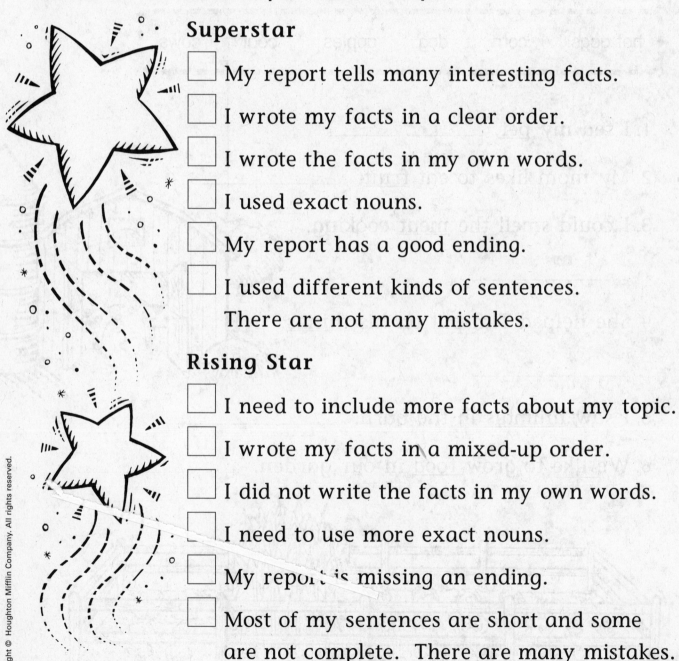

Superstar

☐ My report tells many interesting facts.

☐ I wrote my facts in a clear order.

☐ I wrote the facts in my own words.

☐ I used exact nouns.

☐ My report has a good ending.

☐ I used different kinds of sentences. There are not many mistakes.

Rising Star

☐ I need to include more facts about my topic.

☐ I wrote my facts in a mixed-up order.

☐ I did not write the facts in my own words.

☐ I need to use more exact nouns.

☐ My report is missing an ending.

☐ Most of my sentences are short and some are not complete. There are many mistakes.

Theme 4: **Amazing Animals** 21

**Reading-Writing
Workshop**

Improving Your Writing

Using Exact Nouns

**Read the sentences. Use a word from the box to
change the underlined noun in each sentence to an
exact noun.**

| hot dogs | corn | dog | apples | coat | cows |

1. I fed my <u>pet</u>. _____

2. My mom likes to eat <u>fruit</u>. _____

3. I could smell the <u>meat</u> cooking.

   _____

4. She helped Tim put on his <u>things</u>.

   _____

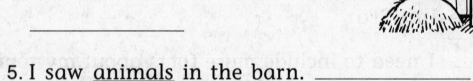

5. I saw <u>animals</u> in the barn. _____

6. We like to grow <u>food</u> in our garden. _____

Name _____

Special Words for Writing

These Spelling Words are words that you use in your writing. Look carefully at how they are spelled. Write the missing letters in the Spelling Words below. Use the words in the box to help you.

Spelling Words

1. done
2. girl
3. found
4. into
5. your
6. around
7. back
8. one
9. some
10. two
11. once
12. I'll

1. f _____ n d   7. s _____ e

2. y o _____ r   8. d _____ e

3. g _____ l   9. t _____ o

4. b _____ k   10. i _____ t _____

5. o _____ e   11. a _____ o u _____ d

6. I' _____   12. o _____ e

Write the Spelling Words on the lines below.

Theme 4: **Amazing Animals** 23

Name _____

Spelling Spree

Write a Spelling Word to complete the sentences.

1. The little ____ went to the zoo.
2. She saw ____ black bears eating fish.
3. Then, ____ chimpanzees jumped up and down.
4. ____ huge hippo was swimming in the water.
5. Snakes were crawling all ____.
6. "I'll come ____ to see the mountain goats," she said.
7. She ran ____ the penguin's house.
8. " ____ bus is waiting," shouted the zookeeper.

Spelling Words

1. done
2. girl
3. found
4. into
5. your
6. around
7. back
8. one
9. some
10. two
11. once
12. I'll

1. _____   5. _____

2. _____   6. _____

3. _____   7. _____

4. _____   8. _____

9. Which Spelling Word is a contraction? _____

10. Which Spelling Word means to find something?

_____

Name _____

Proofreading and Writing

Proofreading Find and circle misspelled Spelling Words in this report. Then write the words.

The earthworm is yor garden's helper. Earthworms crawl arund underground. They dig tunnels by eating, digging, stretching, and squeezing. Ones they mix up all the dirt, the roots of plants can grow.

Earthworms need to stay moist to breathe. They breathe through their skin. They do not come out during the day because they might dry up. They come out at night to find something to eat. When they are dun, they crawl bak into the ground.

Spelling Words

1. done
2. girl
3. found
4. into
5. your
6. around
7. back
8. one
9. some
10. two
11. once
12. I'll

1. _____   3. _____   5. _____

2. _____   4. _____

Write an Animal Note Write a note on another sheet of paper. Tell about an animal you like. Be sure to include some facts about that animal. Start your note with *Dear* and end it with *Your friend,*. Use as many Spelling Words as you can.

Name _____

Letter Changes

Change the dark letter in each word to make a new word. Each word should end with the letters *nd, nt, mp, ng,* or *nk*. The clues will help you.

kin **d** **g**

1. kin**d**   not queen   _____

2. ca**m**e   place for tents   _____

3. thin**g**   you do this   _____
with your brain

4. **p**anes   piece of clothing   _____

5. **c**hime   small ape   _____

6. sin**g**   something to   _____
wash dishes in

7. **l**ane   not water   _____

On the lines below write 3 sentences. Use one of the new words you made in each sentence.

8. _____

_____

_____

_____

Name _____

Ant Funnies

**Write the base word and ending for each word
in dark type.**

1. Let me tell you about the queen ant. She likes
to read **stories** to the other ants.

base word _____ ending _____

2. She likes to eat on silver **dishes**.

base word _____ ending _____

3. She keeps all her food in wooden **boxes**.

base word _____ ending _____

4. Her best friend is the queen of the **flies**.

base word _____ ending _____

**Now read the sentences below. Make the underlined
words mean more than one by adding -s or -es or by
changing the y to i and adding -es. Write the new words.**

5. Ants live in _____. <u>colony</u>

6. Army ants live in _____. <u>jungle</u>

7. Larvae are like ant _____. <u>baby</u>

8. Ants have strong _____. <u>body</u>

Theme 4: **Amazing Animals**   27

Name _____

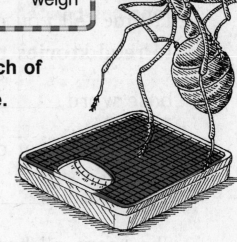

Fancy Ants

Word Bank

| between | care | weigh |

**Find the words in the box that rhyme with each of
the words below. Write the words on the line.**

1. bean _____

2. hair _____

3. stay _____

**Use a word from the box to finish each question.
Then read the answer to each question.**

4. Who can take _____ of a hungry ant?
   the ant's AuNT

5. How do you _____ an ant?
   you cAN'T

6. What does an ant eat as a snack

_____ meals?
   green plANTs

Name _____

How Are They Alike?

Read the questions. Use words from the box to write sentences that answer the questions. The first one has been done for you.

1. Where do ants, prairie dogs, and termites live in groups?

   They live in colonies.
   _____

2. What underground place do ants, cars, and gophers travel through?

   _____

3. What do ants, moths, and other insects have on their heads?

   _____

4. What are mushrooms, molds, and mildew that grow in damp places?

   _____

5. What do silkworms, ants, and butterflies live in as they change and grow?

   _____

6. What are young butterflies, ants, or moths called?

   _____

Name _____

Text Organization Chart

As you read the story, use this chart to help you keep track of what you learn about ants.

Main Idea	Details
Ants make anthills. (pages 64–65)	
Ants have antennae. (pages 66–67)	
Ants work together. (pages 68-69)	
Some ants are called leafcutter ants. (pages 72-73)	

Name _____

Poem Words

Use the two charts to help you get started writing a poem. Write a topic that interests you in each circle. Then list words that go with that topic. For each topic, choose two of those words and list words that rhyme with them. Try to choose rhyming words that will fit with your topic.

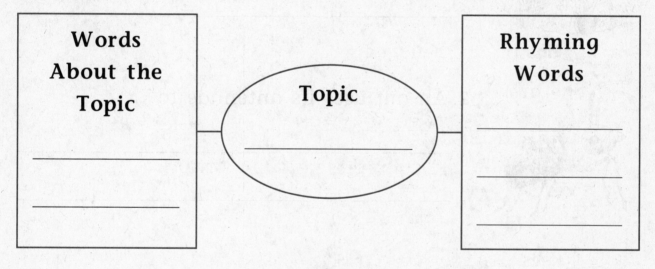

Name _____

About the Story

Look at the picture. Then finish the sentence beside the picture.

1. When you see an anthill, you know that

_____

_____

2. An ant uses its antennae to

_____

_____

3. The ant carries leaves because

_____

_____

4. The ant is "milking" the caterpillar because

_____

_____

Text Organization

Read the article below. Then complete the chart on page 36.

Amazing Beetles

Beetles may be the kings of insects.
Beetles have lived on Earth longer than any
other insect. There are more beetles than any
other kind of insect.

Almost 400,000 kinds of beetles live on
Earth. You need a magnifying glass to see the
smallest beetle. The biggest beetles live in the
jungle. They are six inches long. That's longer
than your hand! Some beetles have shiny green
bodies. Some are plain and brown. You may
have held one kind of beetle in your hand — the
ladybug.

People do many things with beetles. People
with gardens buy boxes of ladybugs. Ladybugs
are good for gardens. They eat insects that hurt
plants. Some people make jewelry from fancy
green beetles. Other people keep beetles for pets.
In some parts of the world, beetles are food. People
eat the beetles.

If all the living creatures in the world were
standing in a line, every fourth creature would
be a beetle. That is a lot of beetles! This is
why the beetle is called the king of insects.

Theme 4: **Amazing Animals**   35

Ant

Comprehension Skill Text Organization (continued)

Name ______________________________

Text Organization continued

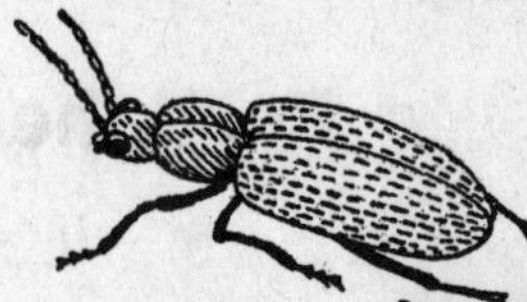

After you've read the article *Amazing Beetles,* complete the chart below.

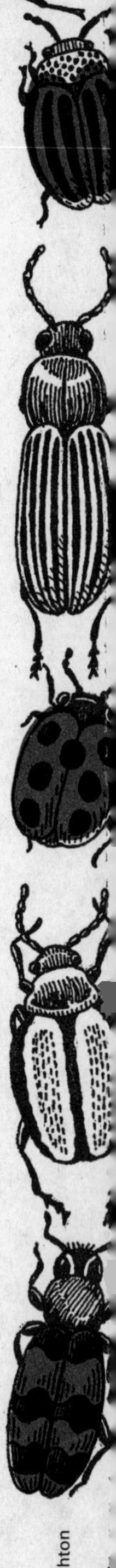

Paragraph 1
Main Idea: ______________________
Details: ______________________
____

Paragraph 2
Main Idea: ______________________
Details: ______________________
____

Paragraph 3
Main Idea: ______________________
Details: ______________________
____

Paragraph 4
Main Idea: ______________________
Details: ______________________

Who Owns What?

Read each group of words below.

Word Bank

queen's eggs   colony's tunnel

worker's leaf   tree's roots

Choose a phrase from the Word Bank that gives the meaning of the two pictures. Write it on the line.

 +  = _____

 + = _____

Now write two sentences. Use one of the phrases at the top of the page in each of your sentences.

_____

_____

_____

_____

Name _____

I or Me?

Read the letter below. The word *I* or the word *me* belongs in each blank space. Rewrite the letter using the words *I* and *me* correctly.

Dear Jamie,

    Yesterday my dad and ____ went to the nature museum. There was a giant ant farm there. Dad and ____ watched the ants for almost an hour. Then the museum guide took Dad and ____ on a tour around the museum. We had so much fun. If we go again, would you like to go with Dad and ____?

               Your friend,

               Brett

_____

_____

_____

_____

_____

_____

Name _____

Ants in the Yard

Read Dora's story. She forgot to add apostrophes to show ownership. Circle the words that need apostrophes.

There are ants in my grandmothers yard. The ant colony is by the trees roots. I like to watch the ants. They are so busy. An ants antennae move all the time. The ants march in long lines. They carry food back to the colony. I once saw them carrying a grasshoppers wing. Another time I saw an ant with a cookie crumb. That was my cookie! That ants dinner was going to be very sweet!

On the lines below, write the words you circled with the words that show what is owned. Remember to add apostrophes to show ownership.

1. _____   4. _____

2. _____   5. _____

3. _____

Name _____

A Walk Outside

Write the word from the box that completes each sentence.

Word Bank

| low | toad | coat | crow | croak | willow |

1. Ben put on his _____ .

2. He walked by a tall _____ tree.

3. He watched a _____ fly out of a tree.

4. It swooped _____ to the ground.

5. Then Ben saw a _____ hopping by the pond.

6. A frog gave a loud _____ as the toad hopped by.

Now write each word under the animal that has the same vowel spelling.

oa

ow

_____   _____

_____   _____

Name _____

Write a Letter

Read this letter that Crane wrote to Bear.

Dear Bear,

Not long ago, you and I were friends. We would play in the field together. Now we are angry with each other. You play alone in half of the meadow, while I play in the other half. It feels like we are at war. I think we should talk about the problem. What do you think?

Sincerely,
Crane

Pretend you are Bear. Write an answer to Crane. Use each of the underlined words in your answer.

Dear Crane,

_____

_____

_____

_____

Sincerely,
Bear

Name _____

Replacing Words

Read each sentence. Replace each word in dark print with a word from the box. Write the letters of that word in the spaces.

Vocabulary

accept   advantage   argument   penalty   quarrel

1. Two bear cubs had a big **disagreement**.

___ ___ ___ ___ ___ ___ ___ ___

2. One cub had an **edge** because he was bigger.

___ ___ ___ ___ ___ ___ ___ ___ ___

3. That cub thought that bigger was better.
   The other cub did not **agree** that this was true.

___ ___ ___ ___ ___ ___

4. Mother Bear heard the **disagreement**.

___ ___ ___ ___ ___ ___ ___ ___

5. She said, "There will be a **punishment** if you
   two cubs do not settle this fight."

___ ___ ___ ___ ___ ___ ___

**On another sheet of paper, write an ending to the story.
Tell how you think the cubs will solve the argument.**

Name _____

Who Owns Something?

► A plural noun means more than one and
  usually ends in **s**.
► A possessive plural noun shows that something
  belongs to more than one person, animal,
  or thing. These nouns usually end in **-s'**.
► Some plural nouns, such as **children**
  and **mice**, do not end in **-s**. To form
  the possessive of these nouns, add **-'s**.

**Read each sentence. Decide if the underlined word
should end with *-s' or -'s* . Write the correct word
and ending on the line.**

<u>players</u>   1. The _____ coach told them
               to kick the ball toward the goal.

<u>referees</u>   2. The _____ whistles blew
               when the ball went into the net.

<u>parents</u>   3. The _____cheers could
               be heard across the field.

<u>children</u>   4. One person handed out all the

               _____ medals.

<u>twins</u>   5. The winning team went to the

               _____ home for a party.

Name _____

In the News

Use the picture to gather information for writing an article about the baseball game. Answer the questions.

Question	Information
Who?	_____
What?	_____
When?	_____
Where?	_____
Why?	_____
How?	_____

Use the information you wrote to write a news article about the game on another sheet of paper. Remember to add details that will catch a reader's interest.

Name _____

Ball Game Clues

Use the clues to complete the puzzle.

1. The Animals and the Birds had a big _____.
2. The _____ thought they were better because they had teeth.
3. The Birds thought they were better because they had _____.
4. They decided to play a ball _____ to decide who was better.
5. Little _____ had both wings and teeth.
6. Bat made the winning _____.
7. The Birds had to fly _____ each winter because they had lost.

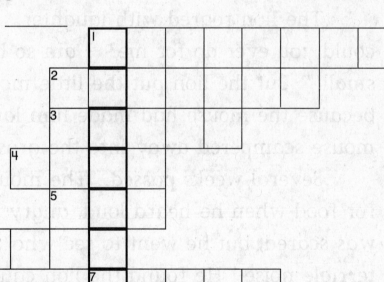

Write the letters from the boxes in dark print to answer this question.

8. Which team won the ball game?

_____ _____ _____ _____ _____ _____ _____ _____

Name _____

Cause ➡ Effect

Read the fable. Then complete the chart on page 53.

The Lion and the Mouse

A lion lay asleep in the sun. A little
mouse darted across the lion's paw. The
lion woke up. He grabbed the tiny mouse
and opened his great, big mouth.

Just as the lion was about to eat him, the
mouse cried, "I didn't mean to wake you up, kind
lion. Please don't eat me! I will always be
thankful. Someday, maybe I will be able to help you."

The lion roared with laughter. He said, "What
could you ever do for me? I am so big! You are so
small." But the lion put the little mouse down,
because the mouse had made him laugh. The
mouse scampered away into the grass.

Several weeks passed. The mouse was looking
for food when he heard loud, angry roars. The mouse
was scared, but he went to see who was making the
terrible noise. He found the lion caught in a hunter's
net. Quickly, the mouse ran to the net. He used
his sharp teeth to chew the threads. The lion was
soon free.

The lion said, "Thank you, little mouse. Sometimes
the smallest friends are the biggest friends."

Name _____

Dictionary Word Match

Most dictionary entries include a picture, an entry word, the meaning of the word, and a sample sentence. Look at the example below. Then read each entry and decide what is missing. Add that part to the entry.

Example

walrus A large sea animal that is related to seals. This mammal has a thick hide, two tusks, and flippers. *A walrus dived into the sea.*

web Thin threads put together in a special way by a spider. *The spider worked all night to spin a web.*

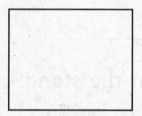

whisker: _____

_____

The baby tried to pull the cat's whisker.

_____ The part that birds, insects, and airplanes use to fly. *The baby bird hurt its wing when it fell out of the nest.*

Name _____

Tongue Twister Sentences

**Write the three rhyming words in
each sentence.**

1. The pig spilled pink ink in the sink.

_____ _____ _____

2. The tiger sent a tent that was bent.

_____ _____ _____

3. The band got a hand from animals sitting in the stand.

_____ _____ _____

4. The cat likes to tramp on the lamp at camp.

_____ _____ _____

5. The skunk fell off the trunk and went kerplunk!

_____ _____ _____

6. The goat with the long beard played the wrong song.

_____ _____ _____

56 Theme 4: **Amazing Animals**

Proofreading and Writing

Proofreading Circle the four Spelling Words in this story that are not spelled correctly. Write each of the words correctly on the lines.

The wind began to blo harder. The air was getting very cold. The birds flew faster. They wanted to get to the ocean before the snoe came. It wouldn't be long now. In fact, there was the water ahead. Soon the birds saw a boat below. All they had to dow was follow the oald bird. He had traveled the path for many years.

Spelling Words

1. boat
2. cold
3. road
4. blow
5. gold
6. old
7. load
8. snow
9. hold
10. most
11. toe*
12. do*

_____ _____

_____ _____

Writing Sentences Some birds fly thousands of miles to get to a warmer place. What would it be like to be one of those birds? Write about it on a separate sheet of paper. Use Spelling Words from the list.

Theme 4: **Amazing Animals**   57

Name _____

Nouns That Belong

▶ A plural noun usually ends in **-s.**

▶ A possessive plural noun shows that something belongs to more than one person, animal, or thing. These nouns usually end in **-s'.**

▶ Some plural nouns, such as **children** and **mice,** do not end in **-s.** To form the possessive, add **-'s.**

Rewrite each sentence. Use the correct possessive noun.

1. The rabbits ears are floppy.

_____

2. The birds babies are hungry.

_____

3. The mice cage is dirty.

_____

4. The sheep wool is soft.

_____

Name _____

Add Details to the Story

**Read the news article. Rewrite sentences on the lines below.
Add details that will make your sentences more interesting.**

Zoo Opens New Snake House

The zoo opened a new snake house. People came to see it on Friday. Visitors found all kinds of snakes. A zookeeper fed the snakes. Mr. Diaz, the zoo manager, said, "People have always wanted to see bigger snakes. We were lucky to have a person donate the money for this exhibit." The zoo is open every day.

1. The zoo opened a new snake house.

_____

2. People came to see it on Friday.

_____

3. Visitors found all kinds of snakes.

_____

4. A zookeeper fed the snakes.

_____

5. The zoo is open every day.

_____

Name _____

More Than One

**Mrs. Howard wrote a list of chores for her pet shop.
She made some mistakes. Read the list. Decide
whether an ' or an 's should be added to the animal
name in each sentence. Rewrite the sentence.**

Things to Do

1. Mix the dogs food in their bowls.

   _____

2. Clean out the cats boxes.

   _____

3. Fill the mice water bottles.

   _____

4. Get a helper to put the puppies toys in the pen.

   _____

5. Wash the walls of the fish tanks.

   _____

60 Theme 4: **Amazing Animals**

Volcano Words

Use a word from the box to complete each sentence.
Write the word in the puzzle.

Vocabulary

disaster   pitch   earthquake   volcano   erupting   lava

Across

3. The ground shakes during an ____.

4. Something that's ____ shoots out rocks or gas.

6. A ____ is a mountain that shoots out melted rock and ash.

Down

1. If there is a ____, there is usually a lot of damage.

2. Hot, melted rock is called ____.

5. When something begins to ____, it begins to move up and down.

Compare Dinosaur Stories

Fill in the chart as you read the stories.

	Little Grunt and the Big Egg	Mighty Dinosaurs
What is the selection about?		
Why did the author write the selection?		
What details did you enjoy reading?		

Problem Solving

For each story, answer the questions on the chart.

	What problems do the story characters face?	How do the characters solve it?
Little Grunt and the Big Egg	_____ _____ _____ _____	_____ _____ _____ _____
The Great Ball Game	_____ _____ _____ _____	_____ _____ _____ _____

How are the solutions in the stories alike?

_____

Name _____

Dinosaur Words

**Read the sentences. Complete them with
the correct words from the box.**

Vocabulary

| reptiles | remains | prey | packs | fossils |

1. Some dinosaurs hunted in _____ to catch their meals.

2. Dinosaur _____ are sometimes bones that have changed to rock.

3. Meat-eating dinosaurs hunt other animals as

   _____.

4. We learn about dinosaurs from their _____.

5. Snakes, turtles, and lizards are not warm-blooded

   creatures. They are all _____.

Choose three words from the box. Use each one in a sentence.

_____

_____

_____

**Monitoring
Student Progress**

Review Phonics *r*-Controlled
Vowel Sounds *or, ore;* Words
with *nd, nt, mp, ng, nk*

Riddles

Write a word from the box to answer each riddle.

Word Bank

snore	winking	humpback	morning
songbird	boring	sandwich	scent

1. I am one kind of whale. What am I? _____

2. I am a good smell. What am I? _____

3. I sing from my nest in the tree.

   What am I? _____

4. This is the time of day that you

   wake up. What am I? _____

5. I am not interesting. What am I? _____

6. You bring me for lunch. What am I? _____

7. I am a noise that someone makes while sleeping.

   What am I? _____

8. This is what happens when I open and close one eye

   quickly. What am I doing? _____

Name _____

Writing Pronouns

Read each sentence. Replace the word or words in
dark print with the pronouns *she, he, it,* or *they.*
Rewrite each sentence.

1. **Little Grunt and George** were pals.

   _____

2. **Aunt Grunt** got food for George.

   _____

3. **The cave** became very crowded.

   _____

4. **Chief Rockhead Grunt** said that George had
   to go.

   _____

5. Later **the Grunts** needed George's help.

   _____

Test Practice

**Read each vocabulary question about *Mighty Dinosaurs*. Use
the three steps you've learned to choose the best answer.
Then fill in the circle beside the best answer.**

1. Read this sentence from the story. "We know a
   lot about dinosaurs from their remains, which
   we have found buried in rocks and beneath
   sand." What does **remains** mean?

   ○ staying late   ○ going away
   ○ parts that are left   ○ pieces of rock

2. The author writes, "Dinosaurs had knobby or pebbly
   skin and laid eggs." Which word means
   the opposite of **knobby**?

   ○ rough   ○ smooth
   ○ pretty   ○ hard

3. On page 127, what does the word **crests** mean?

   ○ teeth for biting or chewing
   ○ body parts that stick up
   ○ leafy plants
   ○ hats to shade their eyes

Continue on page 74.
Theme 4: **Amazing Animals**   **73**

Name _____

Test Practice continued

4. Which word means about the same as **packs** on
   page 128?

   ○ meals
   ○ bundles
   ○ groups
   ○ claws

5. Read this sentence from the story. "Not all
   dinosaurs were fierce hunters." Which word
   means the opposite of **fierce**?

   ○ gentle
   ○ angry
   ○ dangerous
   ○ hungry

6. Read this sentence from the story. "Plant-eating
   dinosaurs needed large amounts of food to give
   them energy." What does **energy** mean?

   ○ a tool to move things around
   ○ a happy feeling
   ○ a light to see with
   ○ the strength to do things

Name _____

Which Word Belongs?

Write a word from the box to complete each sentence.

> **Word Bank**
>
> | fortunate | pumpkin | rowboat | blinking | bandage |
> |---|---|---|---|---|
> | scarecrow | pennies | dishes | barking | shore |

1. A _____ is usually round and orange.

2. He put a _____ on my cut.

3. Give me ten _____, and I'll give you
   a dime.

4. I use my _____ on the lake.

5. Use these _____ to set the table.

6. We walk along the ocean _____.

7. My dog is _____ loudly.

8. We put up a _____ to keep
   the birds away.

9. She will be _____ if she wins
   the race.

10. Are you _____ your eyes?

Name _____

Cause-Effect Chart

Complete the chart for *Little Grunt and the Big Egg*.

Cause	Effect
1. An egg hatches into a baby dinosaur.	_____ _____
2. _____	George is sent away.
3. Little Grunt takes George back to the swamp.	_____ _____
4. _____	The cave begins to shake.
5. George carries the Grunts away from the volcano.	_____ _____

Name _____

Word Search

**Find and circle ten words with *ar, or, er, ir*,
and *ur*. Write the words on the lines below.
Read them to a partner.**

```
l   a   k   d   c   o   s   r   y
b   u   r   n   a   r   t   a   u
i   m   p   o   r   t   a   n   t
r   t   o   w   s   e   r   v   e
d   i   r   t   j   a   t   e   p
p   f   c   a   r   d   n   i   r
h   s   h   o   r   t   g   l   t
```

Words with *ar*	Words with *or*	Words with *er,* *ir*, and *ur*
1. _____	4. _____	7. _____
2. _____	5. _____	8. _____
3. _____	6. _____	9. _____
		10. _____

Name _____

Add an Ending

Finish each sentence. Look at the word ending or syllable in dark print. Add one of the endings from the box to make a word that belongs in the sentence.

Word Bank

-er	-est	-ly	-ful	-ing	-tion	-ture

1. Jan is **plant** _____ a garden.

2. The row of peas is **short** _____ than the row of beans.

3. The row of corn is the **long** _____ row of all.

4. A snake slides **quick** _____ through the garden.

5. The **play** _____ kitten chases the snake.

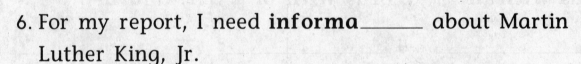

6. For my report, I need **informa** _____ about Martin Luther King, Jr.

7. I will draw a **pic** _____ of him for my report.

8. He wanted all people in this **na** _____ to be free.

Name _____

Word Play

Write the word from the box that fits each definition.

Word Bank

| friend | about | beautiful | near | write |
| believe | watch | surprised | afraid | years |

1. a time word _____

2. not expecting something _____

3. a pal _____

4. to think something will happen _____

5. to look at _____

6. not ugly _____

7. not brave _____

8. not far away _____

9. almost _____

10. what you do with a pen

_____

Name _____

Biography Words

Write the word from the box that means the same
as the underlined word or words in each sentence.

> ## Vocabulary
>
> biography   events   information
> facts   champion   president

1. My sister Elena is the <u>best of
   all</u> on the school math team.   _____

2. Elena tells me about all the
   <u>important things that happen</u>
   at her school.   _____

3. She knows <u>things we know for
   sure</u> about many subjects.   _____

4. She said the <u>leader</u> of the
   United States lives and works
   in the White House.   _____

5. Someday I'm going to write a
   <u>true story of the life</u> of Elena. _____

6. I have plenty of <u>knowledge</u>
   about Elena that I can include.   _____

Biography Notes Chart

Complete this chart as you read about Ellen Ochoa.

Dates (What happened in each year?)
1958 _____
1990 _____
_____
1993 _____
1999 _____

Accomplishments (Six things Ellen did or learned.)
_____
_____
_____
_____
_____
_____

Name _____

Key Events

Fill in the chart by answering the questions about each person.

	Ellen Ochoa	Theodore Roosevelt	Wilma Rudolph
What happened in their childhood?			
What school subjects did they work hard at?			
What did they do when they grew up?			

Name _____

Replace the Pronouns

**Read this book report. Find two places where the
pronoun *he* can be replaced by a noun. Draw a circle
around each pronoun you want to replace.**

George Washington was our first
President. He was born in Virginia in 1732.
He was a general in the army. He led many
battles against Great Britain. He helped to
win freedom for the United States. He has
a monument named after him.

**Rewrite the book report. Replace each pronoun you
circled with *George* or *Washington*.**

_____

_____

_____

_____

_____

_____

_____

Name _____

Biography Notes Chart

Complete this chart about Wilma Rudolph.

Dates (What happened in each year?)

1940 _____

1956 _____

1960 _____

1962 _____

1983 _____

1994 _____

Accomplishments (Four things Wilma did or learned.)

_____

_____

_____

_____

When Did It Happen?

Read the paragraphs about Dr. Seuss. Circle the time-order words and dates.

Dr. Seuss was born on March 2, 1904. He liked to draw. During college, he wrote stories and drew funny pictures. Next, he began creating funny cartoons.

Then Dr. Seuss sold his first cartoon and moved to New York City. Next, he got a job writing ads. Dr. Seuss wrote his first story in 1937. After World War II, he wrote The Cat in the Hat and many other books for children.

Dr. Seuss died on September 24, 1991. Today, children around the world read and love his books.

On another sheet of paper, write five sentences about events in your life. Put them in the order that they happened. Use time-order words.

Name _____

Add Abbreviations

1–6. Read the story. When you find a word missing, choose an abbreviation from the box. Write it on the line. Then read the story again.

Word Bank

| St. | Thurs. | T.C. | Aug. | Mrs. | Mr. |

I saw _____ Clark walking his dog on Elm

_____. He had the letters _____ for Tim Clark

on his shirt pocket. I asked when he was going

to have a yard sale. He said it would be on

_____ 24. Then I stopped to talk with _____

Miller. She invited me to a birthday party for

Sam on _____, July 16.

Now choose two abbreviations. Write a sentence using each one.

7. _____

8. _____

What Do Workers Do?

Use the words in the box to complete each sentence.

Word Bank

houses	play	flowers	beekeeper
teacher	sweet	cleans	waitress

1. A _____ helps children learn to read, write, and spell.

2. A _____ takes our order for food.

3. A _____ has honey to sell.

4. A carpenter helps to make _____.

5. A baker makes _____ food for us to eat.

6. An actor may have a part

   in a _____.

7. A florist sells plants and

   _____.

8. The janitor at school

   _____ the windows.

Name _____

Proofreading and Writing

Proofreading Circle four Spelling Words that are
incorrect. Then write each word correctly.

1. born
2. core
3. short
4. morning
5. fork
6. four
7. horn
8. sport
9. torn
10. sort
11. snore
12. fort

Max was shart for his age but that
never stopped him! He was the surt
of boy who wanted to try everything.

His favorite sport was soccer. So
every murning he would practice
kicking the ball. Then he would run
up and down the field four times.
Max said that he was bourn to play
soccer!

1. _____   3. _____

2. _____   4. _____

Write Questions Write the name of someone you
want to learn more about. List questions you
would like to be able to answer by reading
that person's biography. Use Spelling Words
from the list.

92   Theme 4: **Focus on Biography**

Make It Clear!

Read the story below. Circle the pronouns *he*, *she*, and *they*.

Tom and Kate are twins. Rob and Pam are their brother and sister. Yesterday, he rode his bike to the lake. They went to play soccer at North Field. On Monday, she will finish her clay vase at school. He will take a trumpet lesson.

Rewrite the story on the lines below. Replace *he*, *she*, and *they* with nouns from the story.

_____

_____

_____

_____

_____

_____

Share your story with a partner. They may be different stories, but are both stories clear?

Name _____

Capital Letters Needed

Read the letter. Circle six words that should start with capital letters. Write the words correctly.

May 5, 2004

Dear Grandma,

    I got a puppy for my birthday. I named it rusty. yesterday we bought the puppy a collar that glows in the dark. mom takes the puppy for a walk on maple Street. My sister and i feed the puppy. I hope you can see the puppy soon.

Love,

cora

1. _____   4. _____

2. _____   5. _____

3. _____   6. _____

Name _____

Family Time

Create a funny family story. First, fill in items 1–5. Then use those words to complete the story.

1. Name a person in your family. _____

2. Name a favorite family food. _____

3. Write a verb that names an action that happened in the past. _____

4. Name an object that you find indoors. _____

5. Name an animal. _____

    One day _____ and I decided to make
            1

_____ for the entire family. It was a lot
    2

of work.

    _____ _____ everything into
      1   3

a big bowl. It was very hard to stir. We had to

mix it with a _____ .
             4

    After all that work, nobody wanted to eat

the _____ , so we had to feed it to our pet
      2

_____ . Next time, we'll use a recipe!
  5

Name _____

Family Time

Fill in the chart as you read the stories.

	What family members appear in this theme?	What do family members do together in this theme?
Brothers and Sisters		
Jalapeño Bagels		
Carousel		
Thunder Cake		

Name _____

What Goes with What?

Word Bank

summer	October	number
November	letter	winter

Decide which two words in the list above go with the word in each circle. Write those words in the boxes connected to the circle.

seasons

1. _____

2. _____

things you write

3. _____

4. _____

months of the year

5. _____

6. _____

Name _____

Word Play

Word Bank

trouble	middle	uncle

Draw a line from each word to the meaning of the word.

Words	Meanings
1. trouble	center
2. middle	your mother or father's brother
3. uncle	difficulty

Unscramble each group of letters to make a word.

4. beorult _____

5. ldiemd _____

6. nceul _____

Write the words from the box that rhyme with the words in dark print.

7. double _____

8. fiddle _____

Name _____

Bubbling Words

Circle the word that best completes each sentence.

1. Our family went to the hospital to see
   my aunt's ___ baby.

   newborn   distract   pest

2. The ___ in my class look just alike.

   distract   twins   newborn

3. Fred's ___ brother is learning to drive a car.

   teenage   pest   newborn

4. Rhonda will try to ___ the baby with a toy.

   twins   teenage   distract

**On another sheet of paper, write 4 sentences. Use
one of the words you circled in each sentence.**

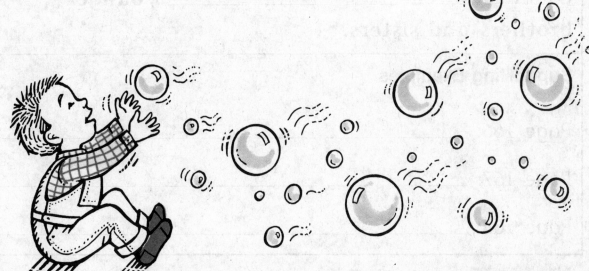

Name _____

Generalizations Chart

Complete the chart below as you read *Brothers and Sisters*.
Complete the generalization sentences and find examples
to support each generalization.

Generalization

A new baby _____ life for
everyone in the family.

Supporting Examples

Page 164: _____

Page 165: _____

Page 166: _____

Generalization

Older children _____ younger
brothers and sisters.

Supporting Examples

Page 166: _____

Page 167: _____

Page 168: _____

---

100   Theme 5: **Family Time**

Taking Turns

Read the story. Then complete the chart on page 106.

Amy and Luke are sister and brother. They take turns when they play games. Sometimes it is easy to take turns. Sometimes it is not.

Dad asks the children if they want to go to the store. Amy and Luke race to the car. They each try to be first to get in the front seat. Dad asks whose turn it is to ride up front. Amy and Luke both say, "Mine!" But Dad says it is Amy's turn.

When Luke and Amy get home from the store, they want to watch a television show. They argue about who gets to choose. Dad asks whose turn it is. Luke and Amy both say, "Mine!" Dad tells Luke to pick the show.

After the show, Mom says she will read them a story. The children want her to read different stories. Mom asks whose turn it is to pick. Luke and Amy both say, "Mine!" Mom says it is Amy's turn.

When Mom finishes the story, she asks whose turn it is to wash the dishes. Amy says, "His!" Luke says, "Hers!" Mom and Dad laugh.

Name _____

Taking Turns continued

After you've read the story, complete the chart below.

Write sentences that will support the generalization.

Generalization:

Brothers and sisters have to take turns.

Supporting Information

1. _____

   _____

2. _____

   _____

3. _____

   _____

4. _____

   _____

5. _____

   _____

Name _____

Teddy Bear Verbs

▶ A verb tells what someone or something does.
A verb can name an action such as **run**, **talk**,
and **smile**.

▶ A verb can also name an activity that cannot
be seen. The words **hear**, **think**, and **worry**
are verbs.

Color the puzzle pieces with verbs brown.

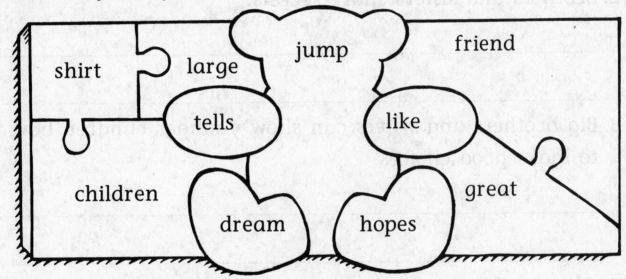

Write a sentence using each of the following verbs.

1. learn _____

2. have _____

3. talk _____

4. run _____

5. climb _____

Name _____

Your Opinion

Rewrite each opinion below. Rewrite the opinion to show that you feel strongly about what you are saying.

1. Older children teach their younger brothers and sisters.

   _____

   _____

2. Brothers and sisters share secrets.

   _____

   _____

3. Big brothers and sisters can show younger children how to make good choices.

   _____

   _____

4. Older children can do extra chores to help their parents.

   _____

   _____

5. An older child can play with younger brothers and sisters.

   _____

   _____

Name _____

Using Exciting Verbs

Read the journal entry below. As you read, think about words that you could use in place of the underlined verbs.

Monday

My alarm did not ring this morning. I <u>got</u> up and saw I was late. I <u>cleaned</u> my face and brushed my teeth. I put on some clean clothes. I <u>went</u> downstairs. I quickly <u>had</u> my breakfast. My Dad <u>said</u>, "Hurry! The bus is coming." I <u>got</u> my backpack. I <u>went</u> to the bus stop as fast as I could. The bus <u>came</u> down the street just as I arrived.

Now fill in the blanks with verbs that will make the writing clearer and more exciting.

Monday

My alarm did not ring this morning. I _____

up and saw I was late. I _____ my face and

brushed my teeth. I put on some clean clothes. I _____

downstairs. I quickly _____ my breakfast. My dad

_____, "Hurry! The bus is coming." I

_____ my backpack. I _____ to the

bus stop as fast as I could. The bus _____ down

the street just as I arrived.

Name _____

Revising Your Personal Narrative

Decide how to make your writing better. Put a check next to the sentences that tell about your narrative.

Superstar

☐ I wrote a good beginning and ending.

☐ I kept to the topic. I told events in order.

☐ I told how I felt about what happened.

☐ I used exact words and clear details.

☐ I wrote complete sentences. There are not many mistakes.

Rising Star

☐ I left out the beginning or the ending.

☐ I did not keep to the topic. I did not write all events in order.

☐ I did not tell how I felt.

☐ I didn't use exact words and details.

☐ Not all my sentences are complete. There are many mistakes.

Name _____

Using Possessive Nouns

Read the sentences. Write the possessive form of the word in ( ).

1. This book belongs to Dad.

   This is _____ book. (Dad)

2. The pail that belongs to Adam is full of water.

   _____ pail is full of water. (Adam)

3. The feet that belong to Mom are sandy.

   _____ feet are sandy. (Mom)

4. The dog that belongs to Adam likes to run.

   _____ dog likes to run. (Adam)

5. They want to ride in the boat that belongs to the girl.

   They want to ride in the _____ boat. (girl)

6. They went home in the car that belongs to Bob.

   They went home in _____ car. (Bob)

Theme 5: **Family Time**   115

Name _____

Special Words for Writing

These Spelling Words are words that you use in your writing. Look carefully at how they are spelled.

Write the missing letters in the Spelling Words below. Use the words in the box to help you.

1. o___r	7. c_____ot
2. t___d____	8. w___o
3. wou___d	9. f___rst
4. a l___t	10. h___r___
5. m___ny	11. fr___ ___nd
6. w___r___	12. c_____ld

Spelling Words

1. who
2. many
3. a lot
4. our
5. cannot
6. here
7. were
8. friend
9. first
10. would
11. today
12. could

Write the Spelling Words on the lines below.

_____ _____ _____

_____ _____ _____

_____ _____

Name _____

Spelling Spree

Use Spelling Words to complete the sentences.

1. We are going to see dinosaurs

   _____ .

2. My _____ is coming too.

3. There will be _____ people
   at the museum.

4. Dad is driving _____ car.

5. Mom says, "We are _____ ."

6. We were _____ in line.

7. We _____ see the dinosaurs
   from far away.

8. The museum guide tells us _____
   about the dinosaurs.

9. Which Spelling Word is a compound word?

   _____

10. Which Spelling Word rhymes with **hood**?

    _____

Spelling Words

1. who
2. many
3. a lot
4. our
5. cannot
6. here
7. were
8. friend
9. first
10. would
11. today
12. could

Name _____

Proofreading and Writing

Proofreading Find and circle misspelled
Spelling Words in this story. Then write each
word correctly.

It was almost time for my party.
Whoo would come first? My baby brother,
Jamal, was sleeping. My aunts, uncles, and
cousins wer coming soon. Meny people
would be in our house today. My frend
Juanita was the first to arrive. We cud
not wait for the party to begin.

Spelling Words

1. who
2. many
3. a lot
4. our
5. cannot
6. here
7. were
8. friend
9. first
10. would
11. today
12. could

1. _____   4. _____

2. _____   5. _____

3. _____

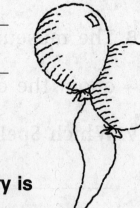

Write a Party Plan Plan a party. Tell who the party is
for, when it will be, who will come, and games you can
play. Write your ideas in sentences. Use as many
Spelling Words as you can.

Name _____

Make New Words

Word Bank

| frost | cream | luck | thirst |

Write the words in the box on the lines below. Next, add *y* to the end of each word. Then use the new words to finish the sentences.

_____   _____

_____   _____

1. Yesterday I needed something to drink. I was

   so hot and _____.

2. I wanted something that was big, cold, and

   _____.

3. My mom mixed ice cream and bananas to

   make a _____ drink.

4. I'm _____ because my

   mom makes me special treats.

On another sheet of paper write two sentences. Use each word below in one of your sentences.

snowy   stormy

Name _____

Un- Matches

Read each of the words in the box. Then read each of the meanings below. On the line beside each meaning, write the word from the box with the same meaning.

Word Bank

unlike	uncooked	unable	uneven
unreal	unbroken	unwell	untrue

1. can't do something _____

2. pretend _____

3. not smooth or straight _____

4. different _____

5. false _____

6. whole _____

7. raw _____

8. sick _____

sad

unhappy

Name _____

Finish Up

Finish each sentence with a word from the box.
You will need to use each word more than once.

Word Bank

aunt	million	pair

1. My father's sister is my _____.

2. My _____ came over to help me
   get ready for my birthday party.

3. She says that the two of us are a great
   _____ of workers.

4. Before we get started, she puts on a
   comfortable _____ of shoes.

5. Then she hands me a _____ of
   scissors and tells me to cut strings for the balloons.

6. I tell her I'm going to cut a _____
   balloon strings.

7. She asks if I think I could count to a _____.

8. I say "Yes," and that I would like to have a
   _____ birthday parties!

Theme 5: **Family Time**   139

Name _____

Words for Bad Days

Use the words in the box to finish the story.

```
                    Vocabulary

   angry          groaned          grumpily
   fussed         grumbled         promised
```

    Joey was having a bad day. He woke up

feeling _____. He had

_____ to help his dad in the

garden. He complained and _____

all day. He talked _____ to his

sister. When his brother asked him to play checkers,

he _____ about never winning.

    Finally his dad came home from work. Joey

_____ and moaned some more.

Then he decided to help his dad plant tomatoes.

As they worked, Joey thought about how good

those tomatoes would taste. For the first time that

day, he smiled.

Name _____

What Do I Think? Chart

As you read, use the chart to keep track of how Alex behaves in the story. Think about how you might have felt if the same thing had happened to you.

What Alex Does	Why Alex Acts This Way
When Alex gets her hair braided, she does not hold still.	_____ _____
Alex opens her first three gifts and complains about them.	_____ _____
After Mother scolds Alex, Alex hugs and thanks her aunts.	_____ _____
Alex opens her last gift and complains angrily.	_____ _____
Alex breaks the carousel and then thinks about fixing it.	_____ _____
When Alex's dad comes home, she greets him and says she is sorry about the carousel.	**What Do I Think About Alex?** _____ _____

Name _____

Puppy Words

The words **puppy** and **baby** have two syllables. The long e sound at the end of a two-syllable word may be spelled **y**.

► The Spelling Word **cookie** does not follow this pattern.

Write the Spelling Words that end with the long e sound spelled y.

_____   _____

_____   _____

_____   _____

_____   _____

_____   _____

Write the Spelling Word that ends with the long e sound that is not spelled with a *y*.

_____

On another sheet of paper, write a silly or funny story. Use four of your Spelling Words in your story.

Name _____

Past or Present?

► A verb is a word that tells what someone or
something does or is.

► Some verbs name actions that are happening
now. Other verbs name actions that happened
in the past.

► The letters **ed** are added to many verbs to
show that something happened in the past.

**Read each sentence. Circle the verb. If the verb tells
about something that happened in the past, put a ✔
on the line.**

1. _____ Alex liked all of her presents.

2. _____ She tells her friends about the pretty

carousel.

3. _____ She wanted her father to be at the

party.

4. _____ She watched the carousel in the dark.

5. _____ The carousel sits on the corner of her

desk.

6. _____ Alex followed the animals outside.

Name _____

Get It Together!

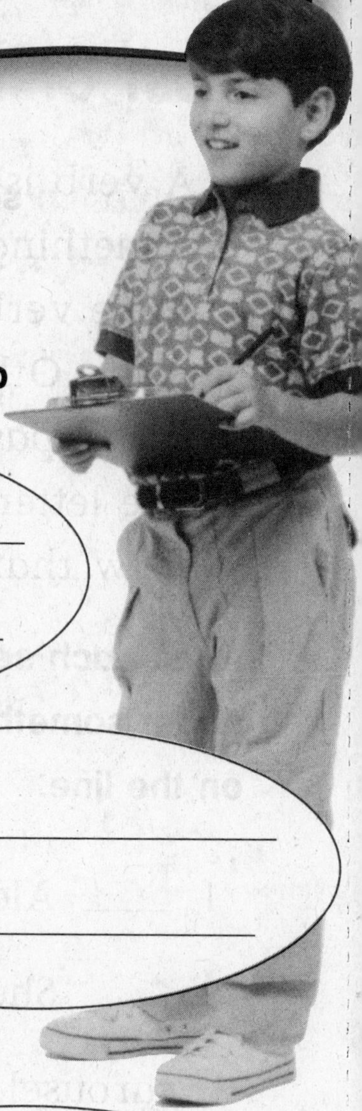

Use the web below to gather information for your
paragraph. In the middle circle, write the subject of
your paragraph. As you gather information about the
subject, write it in the other circles. Then use this web
to help you write your paragraph.

Write one sentence that tells what your paragraph is about.

_____

Name _____

Birthday Blues

Finish each sentence so that it tells what happened in *Carousel*.

1. Alex was unhappy at her birthday party because

_____

2. Alex's mother sent her to bed because

_____

3. Alex whispered, "I'm sorry" to the zebra because

_____

4. Alex's father missed the party because

_____

5. Her father couldn't stay angry about not getting home on time because

_____

6. When Alex's mother winked at Alex and said,

"It got a bit windy in here last night," she

_____

Name _____

Making Judgments

Read the story. Then complete the chart on page 147.

Mike's Bad Day

When Mike got home from school, his Aunt Bea was there.

"Look how much he has grown!" Aunt Bea said. "And how handsome he is!" Mike didn't like people to pay so much attention to him.

"Well, Mike, what do you say?" his mother scolded him.

"Nothing," Mike said in a grumpy voice.

Aunt Bea tried to give him a big hug, but Mike just stood there with his arms at his sides.

Mike's mother said, "Let's go for a walk."

"I don't want to," said Mike. "I have to do my homework. Then I'm going to play with Pepe." Pepe was Mike's best friend.

"But Aunt Bea came a long way to see you," said his mother.

Mike liked his aunt, but he wanted to play.

"No she didn't," said Mike. "She came to see you. All you'll do is talk grown-up talk." Then Mike went to his room and shut the door. He could hear his mother and aunt talking and laughing. He suddenly felt all alone.

Name _____

Keep Them Straight!

Homophones are words that sound the same but have different meanings and spellings. Choose the correct homophone from the box to complete each sentence.

I	eye
four	for
stair	stare
whole	hole

1. The party was going to start at

   _____ o'clock.

   Davey couldn't wait _____ it to start.

2. He sat on a top _____ so he could see the people arrive.

   From there he could _____ at the big present his uncle brought.

3. His mother said, " _____ can't believe you are hiding up there!"

   Davey said, "I'm keeping an _____ on who comes in."

4. Davey's _____ family came to the party.
   The big candle they put on the cake made a

   _____ in the frosting.

Silly Pairs

Use a pair of words from the box to finish each silly sentence.

> puddle beetle   giggle battle   simple riddle
> little bottle   noodle doodle

1. An easy puzzle is a

   _____.

2. A laughing fight is a

   _____.

3. Silly writing with macaroni is a

   _____.

4. A bug in a little pond is a

   _____.

5. A jar that is too small to use is

   a _____.

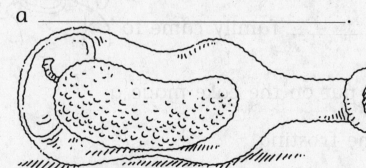

Name _____

Proofreading and Writing

Proofreading Circle four Spelling Words that are spelled wrong in the ad below. Then write each word correctly.

Spelling Words

1. puppy
2. baby
3. lucky
4. happy
5. very
6. lady
7. funny
8. silly
9. many
10. only
11. cookie*

Bert's Pets

Make your son or daughter very

hapy today!

A kitten or pupy is the perfect

birthday gift.

We have manny pets to choose from.

Make today your child's luckee day!

1. _____   3. _____

2. _____   4. _____

Write an Ad On a separate sheet of paper, write your own ad. Make it fun to read. Use Spelling Words from the list.

Name _____

Make a Choice

Choose the best verb to finish each sentence.
Write it on the line.

1. Last week Angie _____ her birthday.

   | celebrates celebrated |

2. Now she thinks she _____ much older.

   | looks   looked |

3. At the party, Angie _____ many presents.

   | opens   opened |

4. She and her friends _____ lots of fun games.

   | plays   played |

5. They _____ party treats.

   | shares   shared |

6. When her baby brother popped a

   balloon, Angie _____ .

   | smiles   smiled |

7. After the party was over, Angie

   _____ her mother.

   | thanks   thanked |

8. She _____ she
   will have another party today!

   | hopes   hoped |

Name _____

Information, Please

Read the information paragraph about emus. Look for ways to combine sentences. Then rewrite the paragraph by combining some of the sentences.

Emus are birds. They are large birds. Emus live mostly in Australia. They have long necks. They have long legs. They can be up to six feet tall. They can weigh up to 75 pounds. Emus can run as fast as 40 miles an hour. Their legs are strong. They can break a fence with one kick. Emus have wings. Emus can't fly. Emus are amazing birds.

_____

_____

_____

_____

_____

_____

Name _____

Make the Writing Better

Read the card Maria has written. Circle the verbs that are not correct. Then write them correctly.

Dear Aunt Ruby,

　　Thank you for the sweater you sent me for my birthday. I am wearing it right now. It looked great with the pants I am wearing.

　　I'm sorry you miss the party yesterday. The day before the party, Mom bakes a perfect cake. We all cheer when she carried it into the dining room. Then Mom and Aunt Julia serves the cake to everyone. Yesterday was a great day. Just thinking about it makes me wanted to have another piece of cake!

　　　　　　　　Your niece,
　　　　　　　　Maria

1. _____   4. _____

2. _____   5. _____

3. _____   6. _____

Thunder Cake

Phonics Skill Base Words
and Endings *-ed, -ing*
(double final consonant)

Name _____

Adding Endings

Write the base word and ending for each underlined word.

1. The rain was <u>beginning</u> to fall fast.

   _____   _____
   base word   ending

2. The girl <u>stepped</u> around the puddles.

   _____   _____
   base word   ending

3. She was <u>getting</u> very wet.

   _____   _____
   base word   ending

4. Lightning <u>ripped</u> across the sky.

   _____   _____
   base word   ending

5. She heard thunder <u>clapping</u> loudly.

   _____   _____
   base word   ending

6. Finally she started <u>running</u>.

   _____   _____
   base word   ending

Theme 5: **Family Time**   155

Name _____

Word Search

Find and circle six words with the silent consonants in *gh*,
kn, or b. Write the words on the lines below.

```
j  y  c  f  k  n  e  e  e
k  l  a  m  b  b  e  f
t  a  u  g  h  t  n  o
l  r  g  k  n  o  c  k
s  l  h  t  k  n  w  o
m  i  t  x  l  i  m  b
```

1. _____

2. _____

3. _____

4. _____

5. _____

6. _____

Name _____

Rhyming Fun

Finish each rhyme with a word from the box.

Word Bank

air	child	heavy	hour

Thunder and lightning? We don't care!

The smell of Thunder Cake is in the _____.

Mix the egg, then add the flour.

We'll eat Thunder Cake in just one _____!

Grandma's Thunder Cake is baked just right.

It's not _____ ; it's sweet and light.

"Come here, _____, and have a taste.

Don't let this Thunder Cake go to waste!"

Name _____

Weather Report

Follow these directions to draw a picture inside the frame.

1. Draw a line for the horizon.
2. Draw storm clouds in the sky.
3. Draw a bolt of lightning coming from the clouds.

Use words from the box to help you answer these questions.

4. What is the weather like in your drawing?

_____

5. Think about the last time there was a storm. What sound did you hear after you saw lightning?

Name _____

Which Verb?

▶ **Is** and **are** tell about something that happens now.

▶ **Was** and **were** tell about something that happened in the past.

▶ **Is** and **was** tell about one thing or person.

▶ **Are** and **were** tell about more than one thing or person.

Draw a line under the correct verb. Then write the sentence correctly.

1. Yesterday the children (was, were) at home.

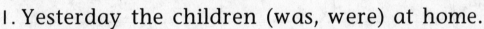

2. Now they (are, were) at Grandma's house.

_____

3. The cake (was, were) in the oven.

_____

4. Grandma, Tom, and Sue (is, are) in the kitchen.

_____

5. Tom (is, are) at the table.

_____

6. What time (is, was) it now?

_____

Name _____

Who's Speaking?

Use this chart to help you describe the speakers you will include in your writing.

	Speaker 1	Speaker 2
Who is the speaker?	_____ _____	_____ _____
Write 3 words to describe the speaker.	_____ _____ _____	_____ _____ _____
What does the speaker want?	_____ _____ _____	_____ _____ _____
How does the speaker talk? (Circle one.)	Long sentences and big words Funny Many describing words	Long sentences and big words Funny Many describing words

Name _____

Letter Home

Here is a letter the girl in *Thunder Cake* might have written. Fill in the missing parts of her letter.

Dear Mama,

Yesterday was a special day. It began to thunder, and I

was so scared that I _____.

Grandma told me we had to _____.

She taught me how to tell _____.

First you see the lightning. Then you _____

_____.

We got eggs and _____ from the barn. Then

we got chocolate, sugar, and flour from the _____.

Last we got tomatoes and _____. Then we made

the cake.

Grandma told me I was brave because I _____

_____. I really did feel brave!

I miss you,

Your daughter

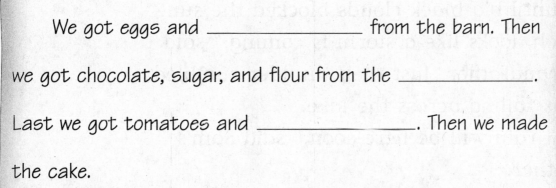

Name _____

Follow the Events

Read the story below.

Fish Story

One sunny afternoon, Sam and his grandfather went fishing. They walked through the woods to the edge of the lake. Sam found a log for them to sit on. His grandfather set up their poles and put worms on the hooks. While they sat on the log fishing, Sam's grandfather told stories.

Soon Sam had a bite on his line. He reeled the line in and caught his first fish. Sam was so excited that he almost fell into the water. His grandfather helped him get the fish off the hook and put it in the bucket. Together they sat talking and fishing until big black clouds blocked the sun.

"Uh-oh, looks like a storm is coming," said Sam's grandfather. Just then thunder rumbled. Rain was falling across the lake.

"That rain will be here soon," said Sam's grandfather.

They packed their things. As they walked back through the woods, the rain began to pour down.

"This looks serious!" said Sam's grandfather.

When they got to the car, they were soaking wet. Sam was cold, but he was happy. He had caught ten fish!

Name _____

Look It Up

Read each word. Can you find it in the dictionary? For some you will need to drop the ending and look up the base word. For each one, write the word you would find in the dictionary.

1. climbing   _____

2. sting   _____

3. knowing   _____

4. chopped   _____

5. thread   _____

6. stepping   _____

7. fanning   _____

8. writing   _____

9. next   _____

10. clogged   _____

Name _____

Matching Rhymes

**Write a word from the box that rhymes with each word
in dark print.**

Word Bank

| sunny | plenty | thirty | bumpy | lobby | nifty |

1. My grandmother owns **twenty** cake pans.

_____

2. Baking is her **hobby**. _____

3. She can bake **fifty** kinds of cakes!

_____

4. I help her wash the **dirty** dishes.

_____

5. We tell **funny** jokes while we wash.

_____

6. I can't be **grumpy** at my

grandmother's farm.

_____

Name _____

Improve the Writing

Read the dialogue. Then rewrite it below, correcting capitals and punctuation that are incorrect.

"Grandma, what were you like when you were a girl? asked Mina.

Oh, about like you, I suppose," she said

"what do you mean" asked Mina.

Grandma looked very serious. "I liked c____ better than carrots. I liked to climb trees. And I asked too many questions.

Mina and her grandma laughed, and thei___ laughs sounded just the same.

_____

_____

_____

_____

_____

_____

_____

_____

Theme 5: **Fan**

Name _____

Past and Present

**Read the biography. Circle the verbs that are used
incorrectly. Write the correct verbs below.**

My grandmother are an amazing person.
She is a nurse when she was young. She were
working in a hospital in India. There is many
patients there who liked her. Some of them
still write to her today. I think they was
lucky to meet her!

1. _____

2. _____

3. _____

4. _____

5. _____

Name _____

Making Connections

Write the word from the box that fits each meaning.

> **Vocabulary**
>
> message   travel   curve   advice   instructions

1. steps for how to do something _ _ _ ( ) _ _ _ _ _ _ ( ) _ _

2. go far away ( ) _ _ _ _ ( )

3. tips from a friend _ _ _ _ _ _

4. a bend or turn _ _ _ _ ( )

5. a short letter or note _ _ _ _ _ _ _

Now use the circled letters to answer this riddle:

Where might you find a message?

6. in a **b** __ __ __ __ __ __

Name _____

What Do I Think?

**Use the charts to keep track of how Julian, Blaise, and
Joy behave. Why do you think they act this way?**

A Curve in the River	
What Julian Does	**Why Julian Acts This Way**
He will not see Gloria after she finds his message.	_____ _____
He goes to see Gloria.	_____ _____
He asks Huey and Gloria to send bottles, too.	_____ _____

Slippery Siblings	
What Blaise and Joy Do	**Why Blaise and Joy Act This Way**
Joy lets Blaise drive during the Empire Games.	_____ _____
Blaise and Joy practice twice a week.	_____ _____

Creativity Chart

**Complete the Creativity Chart below using what you
know about the selections in this theme.**

Selection Titles	What Was Created
Jalapeño Bagels	_____
"Carousel Designed by Kids"	_____
Thunder Cake	_____
A Curve in the River	_____

What creation did you like best? Why?

_____

_____

_____

_____

Name _____

Map the Big Sled Race

Vocabulary

bobsled   catchers   run   course   straightaways

Follow the directions to draw a picture in the frame.

1. Draw a bobsled course with turns and
   straightaways.
2. Draw a bobsled at the top of the run.
3. Draw catchers at the bottom of the course.

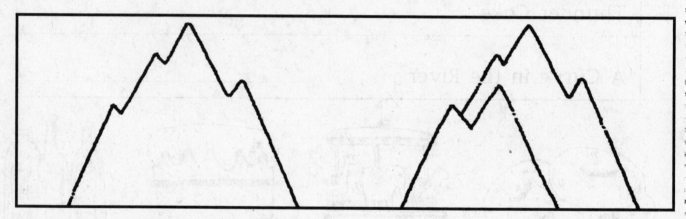

4. Write a short description of a race on your
   course. Use at least three words from the box.

_____

_____

_____

Name _____

Let's Huddle

**Read the sentences below. Write the
two words that make up each contraction.**

1. Let's go, or we will be late!   _____

2. I'll carry that box for you.   _____

3. Please don't touch the glass.   _____

4. Who's your favorite aunt?   _____

5. The dog wouldn't fetch for me.   _____

**Complete the sentences below. Write the correct
word from the box in each blank.**

Word Bank

| huddle | uncle | candle | stable | beagle |

6. That _____ gives off a nice glow.

7. My _____ took me fishing last week.

8. The players met in a _____ .

9. Were those people at the horse _____ ?

10. My pet _____ can be a lot of trouble.

Name _____

Finding Verbs

Read the sentences. Write the verbs that tell about now.

1. A bottle floats down the river.

    _____

2. A girl finds it by the shore.

    _____

3. Frogs hop here and there. _____

4. The girl shows the bottle to some friends.

    _____

5. The friends put letters in the bottles.

    _____

6. A father takes the children to a bridge.

    _____

7. The boys and girls toss the bottles into

    the water. _____

8. The bottles float toward the ocean.

    _____

Name _____

Write the Best Verb

**Choose the best verb to finish each sentence.
Write it on the line.**

1. Yesterday Aldo _____ home.
   (walks, walked)

2. Now he _____ a ride. (wants, wanted)

3. Yesterday the sky _____ blue. (is, was)

4. Now the sky _____ gray. (is, was)

5. Last week Tanya _____ berries.
   (picks, picked)

6. Now she and her brother _____ them with
   cream. (serve, served)

7. Now the blackberries _____ ripe.
   (are, were)

8. Last week some berries _____ still red.
   (are, were)

Name _____

Proofreading and Writing

Proofreading Circle four Spelling Words that
are wrong. Then write each one correctly.

> I hope your'e coming to my house later to
>
> play. Im now the owner of a really cute kitten.
>
> He likes to act sillie. I think you'll like huging him.

1. sister
2. sitting
3. mother
4. I'll
5. you're
6. I'm
7. happy
8. silly
9. hugging
10. it's

1. _____   3. _____

2. _____   4. _____

Take a Look! Write Spelling Words to finish this
story.

My _____ and my _____
              5.   6.

love to bake. Tanya is _____ on the chair.
                                        7.

She looks _____. Someday, _____
                    8.   9.

help too. I think _____ fun to eat what they make!
                              10.

Write a Poem On another sheet of paper, write a poem.
Use the Spelling Review Words.

Test Practice

**Use the three steps you've learned to answer these
questions about *Slippery Siblings*. Make a chart on a
separate paper, and then write your response on the
lines below. Use the checklist to revise your answer.**

1. In what ways does the title *Slippery Siblings*
   describe Blaise and Joy?

_____

_____

_____

_____

_____

_____

_____

Checklist

✔ Did I repeat words from the question at the beginning of my answer?

✔ Can I add more details from what I read to support my answer?

✔ Did I use clear handwriting? Did I make any mistakes?

Continue on page 186.
Theme 5: **Family Time**   **185**

Name _____

Test Practice continued

2. **Connecting/Comparing** Explain how both
   Blaise in *Slippery Siblings* and the girl in
   Thunder Cake use counting to help them.
   Include details from both selections.

_____

_____

_____

_____

_____

_____

_____

_____

Checklist

✔ Did I repeat words from the question at the beginning of my answer?

✔ Can I add more details from what I read to support my answer?

✔ Did I use clear handwriting? Did I make any mistakes?

**Read your answers to Questions 1 and 2 aloud to a
partner. Then discuss the questions on the checklist.
Make any changes that will improve your answers.**

Rhyming Riddles

**Answer each riddle below by writing the
correct word from the box.**

Word Bank

| thought | climb | comb | unknown | bought | thigh |

1. You do this to get up a mountain.

   It rhymes with **time**. _____

2. This is a part of the body that rhymes

   with **pie**. _____

3. This describes a mystery. It rhymes

   with **cone**. _____

4. This is an idea. It rhymes with **not**. _____

5. This helps you look neat. It rhymes with **home**.

   _____

6. This means "got something at a store."

   It rhymes with **not**. _____

Sequence of Events

Read the events from *Slippery Siblings* shown below. Then number the events in the order in which they happened. Look back to the selection if you need help.

_____ Blaise and Joy Bryant win the gold medal at the Empire Games.

_____ Blaise's father takes him bobsledding for the first time.

_____ Blaise and Joy learn to bobsled at the youth bobsled program.

_____ Blaise and Joy Bryant practice to win more gold medals at the next Empire Games.

On a separate sheet of paper, write a paragraph about Blaise and Joy. Retell the events above in your own words. Put the events in order. Use words from the box to make the sequence clear.

Word Bank

the first time   after that   next   in the future

Name _____

Keep Them Straight!

Write the correct homophone to complete each sentence.

1. _____ is a bird feeder in my yard.

| There Their |

2. I watch the birds _____ the window.

| threw through |

3. I _____ that the birds like to eat seeds.

| no know |

4. "Come _____ quickly," said mother.

| here hear |

5. "I see a _____ bird at the feeder," said my mom.

| knew new |

6. Yesterday _____ red birds came to the feeder.

| four for |

7. Randy will _____ a report on birds.

| right write |

8. He _____ like to have a pet bird.

| wood would |

Name _____

What's the Missing Word?

**Read each sentence and the words
in the box. Write the word that
completes each sentence.**

1. A _____ was on the
windowsill.

2. Ed _____ to feed his
dog this morning.

3. His sister ate eggs and toast in
the _____.

4. Barb put a vase of flowers on
the _____.

5. We go swimming at the lake
in _____.

6. I will ride my bike in the
_____.

7. That picture you painted is
_____!

cricket   secret

| unzipped   forgot |

| party   kitchen |

| table   middle |

| perfect   summer |

| driveway   window |

| understand fantastic |

Name _____

Word Meanings

Write a word from the box for each definition.

Word Bank

already	could	front	move	special
began	door	great	other	together

1. started   __ __ __ __ __

2. go from place to place   __ __ __ __

3. opposite of back   __ __ __ __ __

4. wonderful   __ __ __ __ __

5. by this time   __ __ __ __ __ __ __

6. something you can open   __ __ __ __

7. was able to   __ __ __ __ __

8. in the same place   __ __ __ __ __ __ __ __

Write a word from the word box to finish each sentence.

9. I have two pets. One pet is a goldfish,

    and the _____ is a dog.

10. Mom made a _____ cake
    for my birthday.

Name _____

Chapter Book Puzzle

Fill in the puzzle with words from the box that fit the clues.

Word Bank

chapter   character   problem   solution

Across

1. something to which an answer is not known

2. a person in a story

Down

3. a main division of a book

4. an answer to a problem

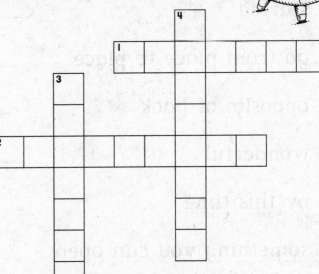

Think of a chapter book you have read. Write the title, the problem characters faced, and the solution.

_____

_____

_____

_____

Name _____

Story Map

Fill in the map for Chapters 1 and 2 of *The Cool Crazy Crickets*.

Characters	_____ _____
Chapter 1 Setting **Problem** **Solution**	_____ _____ _____ _____ _____ _____
Chapter 2 Setting **Problem** **Solution**	_____ _____ _____ _____ _____

Name _____

Key Events

Write a summary for each chapter. In a few sentences, tell the problem, who solves it, and the solution.

Chapter 1: _____

_____

_____

Chapter 2: _____

_____

_____

Chapter 3: _____

_____

_____

Chapter 4: _____

_____

Did you like this story? Why or why not?

_____

_____

Name _____

Plan a Chapter

What will the *Cool Crazy Crickets* do next?
Fill in the chart.

Characters	_____ _____
Setting	_____
Problem	_____ _____
Actions Characters Take to Solve the Problem	1. _____ _____ 2. _____ _____ 3. _____ _____
How the Chapter Ends	_____ _____

Name _____

Homophone Meanings

► Homophones are words that sound alike but do not have the same spelling or meaning.

Write the homophone that goes with each clue.

Spelling Words

1. tail
2. tale
3. plain
4. plane
5. sail
6. sale
7. to
8. too
9. two
10. hole
11. whole

1. an opening into or through something

1. _____

2. all of something

2. _____

3. selling things at low prices

3. _____

4. part of a boat that catches the wind

4. _____

5. not fancy

5. _____

6. people may ride in this in the air

6. _____

7. a number

7. _____

8. also

8. _____

9. a story

9. _____

10. part of an animal

10. _____

Name _____

Telling How

► A word can be added to a sentence to tell
how an action is or was done.

► Example: The twins played **quietly**.

**Read the sentences. Underline the verb.
Circle the word that tells how the action
was done.**

1. A cricket chirped softly.

2. My little sister yelled loudly
   when she saw it.

3. The cricket hopped away quickly.

4. Dave and I gladly helped my
   dad make a tree fort.

5. Dave and I looked proudly at
   our new tree fort.

6. We climbed eagerly up the
   ladder and looked around.

7. My mom carefully planted
   flower seeds near the tree.

8. She patted the soil gently.

Name _____

Story Map

Fill in the map for Chapters 3 and 4 of *The Cool Crazy Crickets*.

Characters	
Chapter 3 Setting	
Problem	
Solution	
Chapter 4 Setting	
Problem	
Solution	

Name _____

Rhyme Time

Write a Spelling Word that rhymes with the word in dark print and makes sense in the sentence.

1. Will you come to the **zoo**, _____?

2. One **mole** ran into the _____.

3. The **train** has _____ seats.

4. We read a _____ about a **whale**.

5. **Who** gave the gift _____ you?

6. She took the **scale** to a yard _____.

7. The dog wagged its _____ when it saw the **pail**.

8. The man pointed to the _____ with his **cane**.

9. The _____ for our boat came in the **mail**.

Write a homophone for each word below.

10. too _____   11. hole _____

_____

Name _____

Characters

Write three things about each person. Tell something
the person does and what the person is like.

Leo _____

_____

_____

Marcus _____

_____

_____

Phoebe _____

_____

_____

Miranda _____

_____

_____

How are all the friends alike? _____

_____

_____

Name _____

Quote Me

Write the words in each speech balloon as a quotation. Add *said* and the speaker's name.

_____

_____

_____

_____

Name _____

Tell Me a Riddle

Write an answer from the box for each riddle.

Word Bank

On your mark, get set, glow.   an angry zebra

Let us hop into the salad.   a newspaper

The spider spied her.   a spelling bee

1. What insect is smarter than a talking parrot?

   _____

2. What is black and white and read all over?

   _____

3. What is black and white and red all over?

   _____

4. What did the lettuce say to the cucumber?

   _____

5. How do you start a firefly race?

   _____

6. Why did the fly fly?

   _____

Name _____

Follow the Path

Read each word on the path. Color one-syllable words
red. Color two-syllable words blue. Color three syllable
words green.

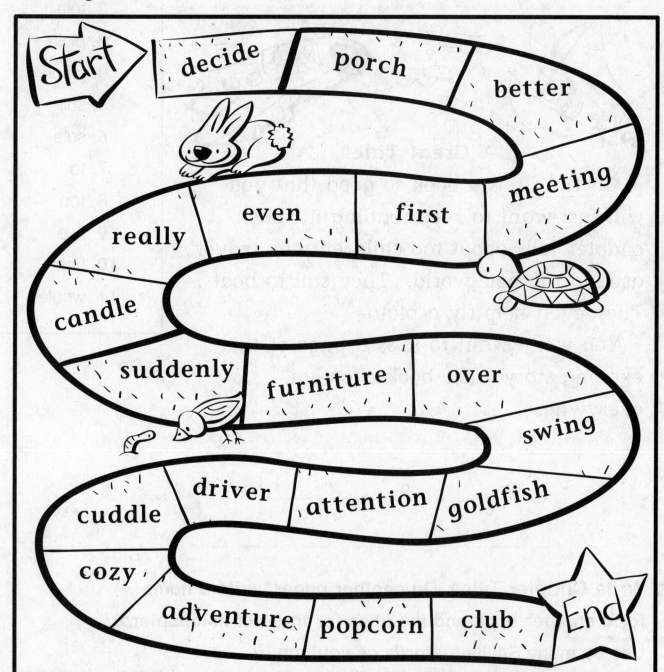

Start

decide   porch   better

meeting

even   first

really

candle

suddenly   furniture   over

swing

driver   attention   goldfish

cuddle

cozy

adventure   popcorn   club

End

Name _____

Proofreading and Writing

Proofreading Circle the four Spelling Words that
are incorrectly spelled. Write each word correctly.

A Great Tale!

On the Go is a book so good that you
will just want to keep reading it. Each
chapter tells about too children who travel
around the hole world. They sail in boats.
They even help fly a plain.

You won't want to miss a page of this
exciting story. The book is on sail
everywhere!

1. _____   3. _____

2. _____   4. _____

Write Chapter Titles On another paper, write a name
for a chapter book and the titles for three of its chapters.
Use as many Spelling Words as you can.

Name _____

How?

1–6. Read the story. Write a word from the box to tell how each action is done. Use each word once.

Word Bank

| quickly | gently | carefully |
| cheerfully | loudly | eagerly |

It is Jan's birthday. She _____ waits

for the mailman. His truck screeches _____

and stops by the mailbox. Jan jumps _____

off the swing and runs to the truck. The mailman

waves _____ to Jan. He hands her a huge

box. Jan _____ opens the box. A teddy

bear is inside! She _____ gives it a hug.

Write two sentences. Use one of the words in the box in each sentence. Underline the verb. Circle the word that tells how.

7. _____

8. _____

Which Verb Belongs?

► Add **s** to verbs that tell about one person.

► Do not add **s** to the verb when using **I**.

► Use **is** to tell about one; use **are** to tell
  about more than one.

Read each sentence. Write the correct verb on the line.

1. The Cool Crazy Crickets

   _____ a box.

   | paints paint |

2. The friends _____
   a nice clubhouse.

   | makes make |

3. Leo's dog _____ the
   club's mascot.

   | is are |

4. Miranda _____ at
   Noodle's trick.

   | laughs laugh |

5. Leo's dad _____ cookies.

   | bakes bake |

6. The chapter books _____
   on the top shelf.

   | is are |

7. I _____ reading books.

   | like likes |

8. A frog and toad _____
   friends in one chapter book.

   | is are |

Name _____

Talent Show

Plan a classroom or school-wide Talent Fair. Use these questions to help you write your invitations.

Where will your Talent Fair take place?

_____

What time will it be?

_____

What day will it be held?

_____

Describe some of the activities that will take place there.

_____

_____

_____

_____

_____

Name _____

Talent Show

Fill in the chart as you read the stories.

	What types of talents did you read about in this theme?	How did talent and hard work help some of the characters in this theme?
The Art Lesson		
Moses Goes to a Concert		
The School Mural		

Name _____

Talented Words

Write the word from the box that completes each sentence.

Word Bank

threw	clues	flew	moon	soup

1. Carla knows all about the stars and

   _____. Someday, she might be an  .

2. Sal likes to follow _____ to solve

   a mystery. Sal thinks he would like to be a  .

3. Keisha likes to make _____.

   She wants to be a .

4. Yesterday, Sam _____ the ball really far.

   He thinks he would like to be a .

5. When Amy went on vacation she _____

   on a plane. Now she is sure she wants to be a .

Name _____

Words with Meaning

Write each word from the box after its meaning.

> **Word Bank**
>
> woman   fair   gold

1. A color that looks like bright yellow metal.

   _____

2. A grown-up girl. _____

3. To treat everyone the same. _____

Use the words in the box to complete the sentences.
Then answer the questions.

Pat and Judy entered a painting contest. Pat's

painting was selected as the winner. A _____

from the art gallery gave Pat a _____

medal. Both Pat and Judy worked hard on their

paintings. Do you think it is _____ that

only one girl received a gold medal? Tell why or

why not on the line below.

_____

Name _____

Picture This

Vocabulary

practice   ruin   smock   copy   powders   chalk   crayons

Use the words in the box to complete the sentences below.

Mickey, the Painter

Mickey loves to draw pictures. He uses

different kinds of art materials. Sometimes he uses

_____ and sometimes he uses

_____. Mostly he uses paint

_____ mixed with water. Mickey

finds time to _____ drawing

every day. He used to _____

pictures that other people had made. Now he

draws his own pictures. He always wears a

_____ when he paints. He

doesn't want to _____ his

clothes by getting paint on them.

Name _____

What the Author Thinks Chart

What the Author Says	What the Author Probably Thinks
Page 353: Tommy drew _____ everywhere he went. **Page 359**: Tommy drew pictures on his _____ .	What does the author think about drawing? _____ _____
Page 362: In kindergarten, the _____ didn't stick to the paper. **Page 363**: In the wind, the paint blew off the _____ .	What does the author think about painting in kindergarten? _____ _____
Page 368: Tommy wanted to use his own sixty-four _____ . **Page 373**: Tommy told the art teacher, "Real artists don't _____ ."	What does the author think about real artists? _____ _____

Name _____

Getting Started

Look at the comic strip to find out how powder becomes
paint. Write down the steps.

How to Mix Paint

First
_____
_____

Next
_____
_____

Now
_____
_____

Use the information to write a paragraph that explains how to
make paint from a powder mix. Write your paragraph on another
sheet of paper.

Name _____

Story Frame

Complete the story frame.

Tommy loved to _____ pictures.

He wanted to be an _____ when he

grew up. His twin cousins told him not to copy and

to _____ drawing pictures. Tommy

wanted to take art _____ at school.

He had to wait until _____ grade.

When the art teacher came, the children had to use

school crayons, copy a picture, and draw on one

piece of _____. Tommy would

not draw. The teachers said that it would not be

_____ for Tommy to do something

different. Finally, his teachers agreed that after

Tommy made a Pilgrim picture, he could use his own

box of _____ and draw a second

picture on another sheet of paper.

Name _____

Author's Viewpoint

Read the story. Then answer the questions on page 218.

Lana and the Art Contest

I was working on a math problem when Mr. Albert, my teacher, walked back into the classroom. He was smiling. "Lana, I have some great news for you. Your painting of a sailboat won first prize in the school's art contest. We would like to frame your painting and hang it in the office."

I gasped with surprise. I had forgotten about the painting I turned in last month.

"The school wants to keep my painting?" I asked. "I would love that! Thank you for telling me such exciting news, Mr. Albert!"

The bell rang. I ran to my desk and shoved the books into my bag. I couldn't wait to tell my mom the news. I ran home so fast that I got an ache in my side.

As soon as I opened the door, I shouted. "Mom, where are you? I won! I won the school art contest! They want to hang my painting in the office."

Mom smiled and hugged me. "You are a very good artist," she said. "Your hours of practice have been worth the time. I am so proud of you."

Name _____

Author's Viewpoint continued

After you've read the story about Lana and the art contest, answer the questions below.

1. How does the author feel about winning the prize?

_____

_____

2. Write two words the author used to show these feelings.

_____

_____

3. Write two things the author did that show these feelings.

_____

_____

4. What else might the author have done to show her feelings?

_____

_____

218 Theme 6: **Talent Show**

Name _____

Show the Past Without *-ed*

Many verbs add **-ed** to the end to show past action.

► Verbs that do not add **-ed** to show past action do not follow a pattern or rule for their spelling changes.

Write the word that completes each sentence.

1. Allison and Josie are lucky, because

   they _____ an artist now.

know   knew

2. They _____ art lessons from
   her each week.

take   took

3. Today they cannot _____
   to their lesson.

go   went

4. Last week they _____
   pictures of flowers.

draw   drew

5. Last month they _____
   clay animals.

make   made

6. Allison and Josie _____

   to try something new today.

get   got

Name _____

Complete the Sentence

**Read the sentences and the sentence parts. Rewrite
the parts so that they are complete sentences.**

How Maria Makes a Clay Animal

1. First, Maria gets a lump of clay.
2. Shapes the clay into a ball.

_____

_____

3. Next she makes the animal's body.
4. Then the head and legs.

_____

_____

5. Uses little pieces of clay for ears and a tail.

_____

_____

6. Finally, the clay animal.

_____

_____

Name _____

Irregular Verbs

When Olivia visited her grandmother, she wrote this postcard. She made some mistakes. Find and circle four verbs that should be written to show the past. Write them correctly.

Dear Benjy,

     Grandma and I go to New York City last week. We run to catch the bus to the art museum. I see some really big paintings at the museum. An artist was there. He give me a box of crayons and told me I could be an artist someday, too. Now I draw all the time! When I come home, we can draw pictures together.

        Your best friend,

        Olivia

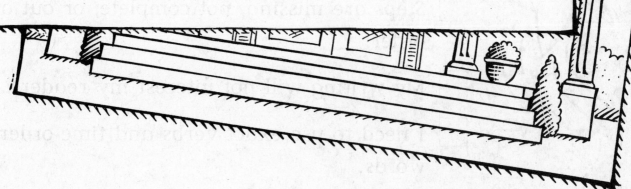

1. _____   3. _____

2. _____   4. _____

Name _____

Revising Your Instructions

Decide how to make your writing better. Put a check next to the sentences that tell about your instructions.

Superstar

☐ My beginning names my topic.

☐ I included all the steps. I told everything about each step and wrote them in order.

☐ My writing will interest my readers.

☐ I used exact verbs and time-order words such as **first**, **next**, **then**, and **finally**.

☐ Sentences vary. There are few mistakes.

Rising Star

☐ My beginning does not name my topic.

☐ Steps are missing, not complete, or out of order.

☐ My writing will not interest my readers.

☐ I need to use exact verbs and time-order words.

☐ My sentences sound the same. There are many mistakes.

Name _____

How to Grow a Sunflower

Cross out the verb in each step. Write the exact verb that best completes each step.

Word Bank

place	dig	shovel

1. First, make a hole. _____

2. Next, get the seed in the hole.

   _____

3. Then, put dirt on the seed.

   _____

Write a sentence for a final step in growing a sunflower. Use an exact verb.

_____

_____

_____

_____

Name _____

Spelling Words

These Spelling Words are words that you use in your writing. Look carefully at how they are spelled.

Write the missing letters in the Spelling Words below. Use the words in the box to help you.

1. s t _____ ted

2. tr _____ d

3. o _____ er

4. com _____

5. p _____ ple

6. s ___ met ___ ing

7. s _____ ool

8. outs _____ e

9. go _____ g

10. n ___ w

11. v ___ ry

12. n ___ v ___ r

Spelling Words

1. tried
2. never
3. going
4. outside
5. coming
6. new
7. very
8. school
9. other
10. started
11. something
12. people

Write the Spelling Words below.

_____   _____

_____   _____

_____   _____

_____   _____

_____   _____

_____   _____

Name _____

Spelling Spree

Write a Spelling word in the star for each clue.

1. a place to learn   4. not old
2. to begin   5. moving toward
3. moving away   6. persons

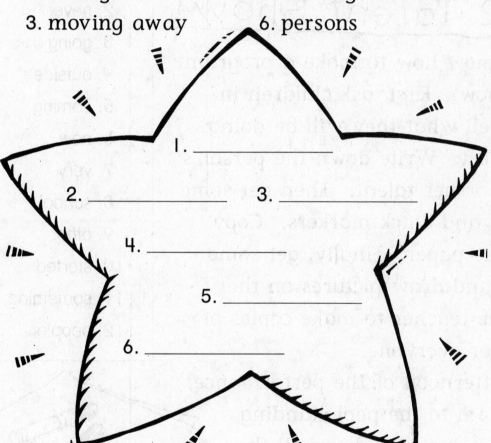

1. tried
2. never
3. going
4. outside
5. coming
6. new
7. very
8. school
9. other
10. started
11. something
12. people

1. _____
2. _____   3. _____
4. _____
5. _____
6. _____

Write a Spelling Word to complete each sentence.

7. We _____ to sing a song.

8. But _____ went wrong.

9. The piano player _____ came.

10. We were _____ sad.

Theme 6: **Talent Show**   229

Name _____

Proofreading and Writing

Proofreading Find and circle misspelled Spelling Words below. Then write each word correctly.

Grade 2 Talent Show

Do you know how to make a program for a talent show? First, ask children in your class to tell what they will be doing. Next, make a list. Write down the person's name and his or her talent. Then get some paper and red and black markers. Copy the list onto the paper. Finally, get some otha markers and draw pictures on the paper. Ask the teacher to make copies of the program for everyone.

On the afternoon of the performance, give the program to the pepl standing outsid the classroom. We hope all the parents are comeing. We have tryed our best to put on a great show.

Spelling Words

1. tried
2. never
3. going
4. outside
5. coming
6. new
7. very
8. school
9. other
10. started
11. something
12. people

1. _____ 4. _____

2. _____ 5. _____

3. _____

Name _____

Sorting Long *i* Words

Write each word from the box under a word that rhymes and
that spells the long *i* sound the same way.

Word Bank

bright	die	fright	lie
might	sigh	pie	tight

knight

_____

_____

_____

_____

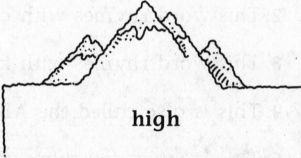

high

_____

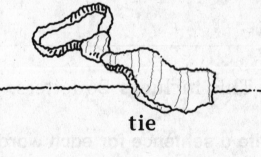

tie

_____

_____

Name _____

Word Wizard

Write the word from the box that goes with each clue.

Word Bank

| heart | mind | alphabet |

ABCDEFGHIJKLMNOPQRSTUVWXYZ

1. This word has three syllables. _____

2. This word rhymes with **cart**. _____

3. This word rhymes with **kind**. _____

4. This is also called the ABC's. _____

5. This is what you think with. _____

6. This is the thing that pumps blood through your body.

_____

7. This includes 26 letters. _____

Write a sentence for each word in the box.

8. _____

9. _____

10. _____

Name _____

Questions and Answers

Read what Nancy asked John about his deaf sister.
Finish John's answers using words from the box.

Word Bank

deaf	vibration	signs
percussion	instruments	hearing

Nancy: What kind of problem does your sister have?

John: My sister is _____ .

Nancy: What does that mean?

John: She has a problem with her

_____ .

Nancy: How do you talk to her?

John: She _____ words with her hands.

Nancy: If your sister can't hear, how can she enjoy music?

John: She feels the _____ from
the instruments.

Nancy: Which _____
does she like?

John: She told me she likes all the
_____ instruments.

Theme 6: **Talent Show** 233

Name _____

Noting Details Chart

As you read the story, complete the chart below.
Find details to support each statement.

Details Chart
Moses can't hear the sounds he makes on the drum. (page 393)
Mr. Samuels's friend is a percussionist. (pages 400 and 402)
The percussionist and children feel the music at the concert. (pages 408–409)
The children meet the percussionist. (pages 410–413)

Name _____

Long *i* Words

Each Spelling Word has the long **i** sound. This vowel sound may be spelled **i**, **y**, or **igh**. The words **eye** and **buy** also have the long **i** sound, but they are spelled differently.

Write each Spelling Word in the column with the same long *i* spelling.

1. sky
2. find
3. night
4. high
5. fly
6. try
7. light
8. dry
9. right
10. mind
11. eye*
12. buy*

long *i*
spelled *y*

long *i* sound
spelled *igh*

_____   _____

_____   _____

_____   _____

_____

long *i* sound
spelled *i*

_____   _____

Write a Spelling Word to finish each sentence. Choose a word that has a star next to it.

1. I went to the store to _____ a kite.

2. Don't put a sharp pencil near your _____.

Name _____

Colorful Adjectives

Color red all the puzzle pieces that have adjectives written on them.

An **adjective** tells about a noun. Some adjectives tell what kind or how many.

▶ The words **a**, **an**, and **the** do not do this. They are special adjectives.

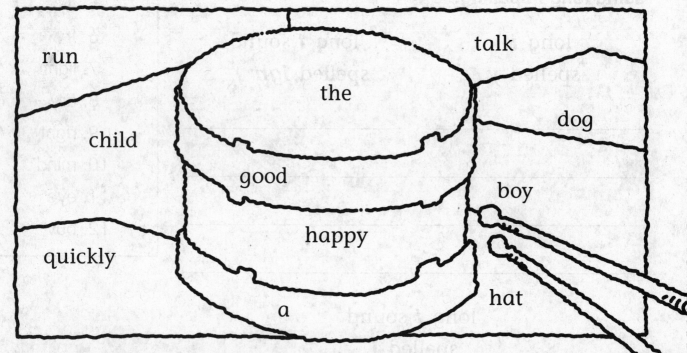

run

talk

the

child

dog

good

boy

happy

quickly

hat

a

Write an adjective to complete each sentence.

1. There are _____ musicians in the band.

2. _____ conductor is their leader.

3. The musicians play _____ music.

4. They play in a _____ concert hall.

Name _____

Planning a Summary

Plan a summary of a story you have read. Answer the questions below.

Who are the main characters?
_____

Where does the story take place?
_____

What is the problem in the story? (Look at the beginning of the story.)
_____

What happens when the characters try to solve the problem? (Look at the middle of the story.)
_____

How is the problem solved? (Look at the end of the story.)
_____

Name _____

Connecting Story Ideas

Put together the two pieces of each sentence to tell about the story. Write the complete sentences.

Moses plays a drum	even though he's deaf.
Moses feels the music	by working hard.
Moses used the balloon	through his hands and feet.
Ms. Elwyn became a percussionist	to feel the vibrations.

1. _____

   _____

2. _____

   _____

3. _____

   _____

4. _____

   _____

Name _____

Noting Details

Read the information below. Complete the chart on page 240.

The Dinosaur Museum

General Information

The museum is open Monday through
Friday from 8 A.M. until 5 P.M. The cost for
having a guide take your class on a tour of
the museum is $50. If you need additional
information, please call 555-1212.

Exhibits

Dinosaurs once roamed Earth. At the
museum, you will see many different kinds
of dinosaurs, including baby dinosaurs and
dinosaur eggs. You will even see real
dinosaur footprints made in stone!

Rules

We have a few important rules at the
museum. Food and drinks should not be
brought into the building. The class must
stay with the guide so that students don't
get lost in the museum. Please do not touch
the exhibits since they can be damaged.
Thank you for your cooperation.

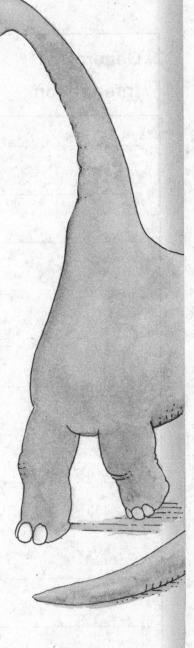

Name _____

Noting Details continued

After you've read the information on page 239, complete
this chart. Give details about the Dinosaur Museum.

General Information	Exhibits	Rules
_____	_____	_____
_____	_____	_____
_____	_____	_____
_____	_____	_____
_____	_____	_____
_____	_____	_____
_____	_____	_____
_____	_____	_____
_____	_____	_____
_____	_____	_____

Name _____

Spelling Spree

Write a Spelling Word for each clue in the puzzle.

Across

1. I will _____ to do my best.

2. Did you _____ your lost pencil?

3. The stars shine at _____.

4. Mom wants me to _____ the dishes.

5. Do you _____ sharing your
   book with me?

7. I see better with my left _____.

Down

2. I wish I could _____ like a bird.

6. I will save money
   to _____ that new toy.

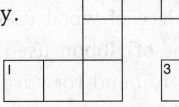

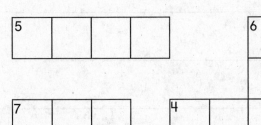

Name _____

What Do You Mean?

Read the different meanings for each word.

Then write a sentence for each meaning.

Example: **play**

A **play** is a kind of story that people act in.

To **play** is to have fun.

My sister is acting in the school **play**.

My brother likes to **play** checkers.

wind

> The **wind** is air that moves or blows.
>
> To **wind** something is to twist it around.

1. _____

2. _____

bow

> A **bow** is the piece of wood used to play a violin.
>
> A **bow** is a type of ribbon used for decoration.
>
> To **bow** means to bend forward at the waist.

3. _____

4. _____

5. _____

Cool Vowel Pairs

**Read the silly sentences. Circle the words that have the vowel
sound you hear in *soon*.**

1. A boot flew over the moon.

2. Jill ate her blue soup.

3. Sam threw a tree into his room.

4. The group of birds sat on a new statue.

**Now write each circled word under the word that
spells the vowel sound the same way.**

spoon

stew

_____

_____

_____

_____

_____

_____

glue

group

_____

_____

_____

_____

Name _____

Proofreading and Writing

Proofreading Find and circle four Spelling Words
that are spelled wrong in the poem. Then write each
word correctly.

Spelling Words

If I Could Fly

I wish I could fly
Wherever I please,
Hygh up in the skye
And over tall trees.

Way up I would go
As lite as a bird,
Then swoop way down low
And never be heard.

I'd turn to the left
And turn to the rit.
I'd fly all day long
And into the night.

1. sky
2. find
3. night
4. high
5. fly
6. try
7. light
8. dry
9. right
10. mind
11. eye*
12. buy*

1. _____   3. _____

2. _____   4. _____

 Write a Poem Write a poem using Spelling Words from
the list. Write your poem on a separate piece of paper.

Hunting for Adjectives

Find and circle eight adjectives in the sentences below.

1. Three big drums sat on the quiet stage.

2. All of a sudden, Lisa started banging

   on two drums.

3. The loud noise surprised everyone.

Now write each adjective under the words that tell about the adjective.

What Kind?	How Many?	Special Adjectives (a, an, the)

Make It Short

Write a sentence that summarizes each paragraph below.

Kites have been around for a long time. They have also carried special instruments to learn more about weather. Some kites were even used to make signals during wars.

1. _____

_____

Porcupine fish get their name from their sharp spines. They are able to puff themselves up with air or water. They can make themselves twice as big as they usually are.

2. _____

_____

Here are some things that will help you do your best when you take a test. First, listen carefully to the directions before beginning. Second, read all questions and answers carefully. Third, take time to check your answers.

3. _____

_____

Name _____

Practice with Adjectives

Rena wants her parents to let her take piano lessons. She made this list to convince them. Make each sentence on her list more interesting by adding adjectives.

1. I will learn how to play

_____ music.

2. I will practice _____ hours every day.

3. Lessons will only cost _____ dollars.

4. I can play _____ piano at concerts.

5. I will give a _____ concert each year.

Name _____

Adding Endings

Add the *-ed* and *-ing* endings to each base word.

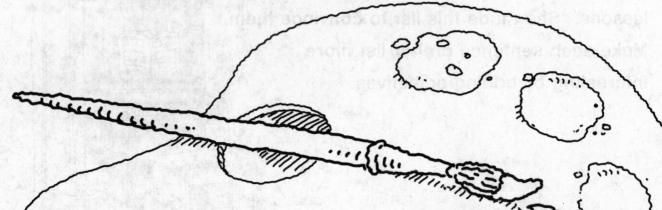

Base Word	+ -ed	+ -ing
smile	_____	_____
trace	_____	_____
trade	_____	_____
vote	_____	_____
raise	_____	_____
skate	_____	_____
slice	_____	_____
whine	_____	_____
rake	_____	_____

Name _____

Using Words

Follow the directions below.

> neighbor   below   should

1. Circle the word that means **under**.
2. Underline the word that means **a person who lives nearby**.
3. Draw a box around the word that rhymes with **would**.

Use words from the box to complete the sentences and question below.

1. Jason lives next door to Kayla. Jason is

   Kayla's _____ .

2. Kayla lets Jason's cat sleep under her window.

   The cat sleeps _____
   the window.

3. Kayla is a good neighbor to Jason. What

   _____ Jason be to Kayla?

Name _____

Match Up

Draw a line from each word to its meaning.

1. event   a good feeling about oneself

2. mural   a huge wall painting

3. pride   a picture of a view

4. project   a job that takes several days to do

5. scene   quickly made drawings

6. sketches   something that happens

Use the words above to fill in the blanks.

The science fair is a big _____. This

year Evelyn worked on a special _____. She

made a volcano. First, she made some _____

to show how the volcano would look.

That day, she spoke with _____ when

she told the judges about her volcano. Next month Evelyn

is going to do a project for the art fair. She is going to

paint a _____ of a snow _____.

Name _____

Large, Larger, Largest

Add **-er** to adjectives to compare two people or things.
Add **-est** to adjectives to compare more than two people or things.

Draw pictures to show the difference among the adjectives.

Example:		
large	larger	largest
1. small	smaller	smallest
2. big	bigger	biggest
3. tall	taller	tallest

Name _____

Alike or Different?

**Think of two stories you have read. Use the chart to tell
how the stories are different and how they are the same.**

	Same	
Different		**Different**
Title of Story 1:		Title of Story 2:
_____	_____	_____
_____	_____	_____
_____	_____	_____
_____	_____	_____
_____	_____	_____
_____	_____	_____
_____	_____	_____
_____	_____	_____

Name _____

Story Sense

Write *True* or *Not True* after each sentence.

1. Mei Lee's idea was to paint a mural. _____

2. Mei Lee got her idea from a picture in a book.

   _____

3. The class decided which idea to use by picking

   a slip from a basket. _____

4. Twenty-five people voted for the mural.

   _____

5. All the children in Mei Lee's class worked on

   the mural. _____

6. Parents were not allowed to help the children

   work on the mural. _____

7. Children, parents, and other visitors came to

   the open house. _____

8. The people cheered when Mr. Ford told

   about the mural. _____

Name _____

Problem Solving

Read this story. Complete the chart on page 257.

Working It Out

Lane and Frank were working on a school project. When they began the project, they had some problems. Lane wanted to build a castle. Frank wanted to build a fort. Lane had an idea. She wrote "castle" and "fort" on two strips of paper. She folded the strips and put them in a box. Frank picked the strip that said "castle."

Next the children drew sketches of the castle. Frank's sketch was very different from Lane's. Frank sketched a new picture that used both of their ideas. Lane liked the new plan.

Then the children talked about what to use to make the castle. Frank suggested cardboard. He wanted to glue sand onto the cardboard to make the castle look like stone. But the sand would not stick. Lane said they should use sandpaper instead. The sandpaper worked much better.

The castle was finally done, but it tilted to one side. Frank thought he knew how to fix it. He got a piece of wood. Lane helped him prop up the castle with the wood.

Name _____

Picking Meanings

Read the words and their meanings. Decide which meaning fits each sentence. Write the correct meaning.

band	past	pick
1. a musical group	1. to go beside	1. to choose
2. a stripe	2. the time in which something has already happened	2. to pull off or gather one by one

1. Mandy painted a **band** of green across the top of

   the mural. _____

2. The school **band** played at the football game.

   _____

3. Omar walked **past** the water fountain on his way

   to class. _____

4. The story takes place 100 years in the **past**.

   _____

5. The children like to **pick** apples off the tree.

   _____

6. Connor didn't know which toy to **pick**.

   _____

Name _____

Long *i*

Use words from the box to complete this letter from one friend to another.

cried
fight
dried
might
night
sigh
tight
tried

Dear Ashley,

   Last _____ my cousins

came to visit. We had so much fun. First we

_____ to scare each other with

scary stories. My little sister was so scared

she almost _____. Then we had

a pillow _____. When my mother

saw the mess in the living room, she just gave a

big _____. My cousins

_____ come back next month.

I hope you can come and visit me.

                              Your friend,
                              Terry

Write a reply on a separate sheet of paper.
Use some of the words from the box.

Proofreading and Writing

Proofreading Irene wrote a postcard to her
uncle about a trip to the zoo. Circle four
misspelled Spelling Words in the postcard.
Write each word correctly.

Dear Uncle Howard,

     I likd going to the zoo. It was fun. We
saw all kinds of animals. We saw a baby kangaroo
ridding in its mother's pouch. We also saw two lion
cubs. They were so cute when they chaseed each
other. Billy was makeing faces at the monkeys, but
they didn't seem to mind. The monkeys were using
their tails to hang from trees.

.

                    Your friend,

                    Terry

Spelling Words
1. liked
2. hoping
3. baked
4. using
5. chased
6. making
7. closed
8. hiding
9. named
10. riding

1. _____ 3. _____

2. _____ 4. _____

Write a Postcard On a separate piece of paper, write a
postcard to a friend or family member describing a trip.
Use Spelling Words from the list.

Name _____

Endings That Compare

Write a word from the box to complete each sentence.

Word Bank

| tallest | thinner | slowest | sillier | closest |

1. The horse looks _____ than the clown.

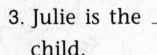

2. The toy car is _____ to the box.

3. Julie is the _____ child.

4. The snake is _____ than the fat lizard.

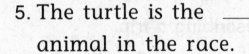

5. The turtle is the _____ animal in the race.

Name _____

Story Comparisons

Cassie and Juan have each read a folktale. Both
stories are about a rabbit that is in a race with
a turtle. In Cassie's story, the two animals decide to
have some fun by racing each other. In Juan's story,
the two animals decide to have a race to show who
is better. At the end of Cassie's folktale, the rabbit
wins the race. At the end of Juan's folktale, the
turtle tricks the rabbit and wins the race.

**Write what is similar and what is different about the stories that
Cassie and Juan read.**

Cassie's Story	Both	Juan's Story
_____	_____	_____
_____	_____	_____
_____	_____	_____
_____	_____	_____
_____	_____	_____
_____	_____	_____

Bouncing Adjectives

Read the story about a basketball game. Circle four adjectives that are not used correctly. Write them correctly.

Sandy and her parents wanted to see Sandy's brother Randall play in the basketball game. The crowd at the gym was biggest than the crowd last week. Sandy sat with her friends. Her mom and dad sat in a row of seats that was up highest. Soon the players entered the gym. The fast player of all was the first one to enter the gym. The other players followed. Some fans cheered for the Dragons. Others cheered for the Bears. The Dragons' fans made the loud cheers of all. The game was about to begin.

1. _____

2. _____

3. _____

4. _____

Name _____

Circus Words

Fill in each blank with a word from the box.

············· Vocabulary ·············

contraption   performance   athletic   circus   somersaults   pyramid

Dear Aunt Frieda,   June 24, 2004

   The _____ came into town last night.
Mom and Dad took Luke and me there today. The

clowns gave a funny _____.
   The acrobats tumbled across the floor doing

_____. Five acrobats got on their hands and

knees to form a human _____. They were so

_____ that they made the stunts look easy!
   Luke liked the trapeze artists. One lady used a

_____ that helped her fly through the air.
We all had a great time!

                              Love,
                              Laura

Story Map

Complete the map as you read the selections.

Join the Circus!		Raymond's Best Summer
_____ _____	**Who?**	_____ _____
_____ _____	**Where?**	_____ _____
_____ _____	**Beginning**	_____ _____
_____ _____	**Middle**	_____ _____
_____ _____	**End**	_____ _____

Details Chart

Fill in the chart. Write two details about each sentence.

Join the Circus!	The Art Lesson
Zhang Jin works hard. 1._____ _____ _____ 2._____ _____	Tommy works hard. 3._____ _____ _____ 4._____ _____
Zhang Jin enjoys being in the circus. 5._____ _____ _____ 6._____ _____	Tommy likes art and wants to be an artist. 7._____ _____ _____ 8._____ _____

Name _____

Swimming Words

Read this interview. Use words from the box to complete the questions and Ned's answers.

Vocabulary

certificate   intermediate   paces   demonstration   ability   laps

Tammy: Why did you start swimming?

Ned: My mom thought that I had swimming

_____. I passed my beginner

test and got my _____. Then I

moved up to the _____ level.

Tammy: How often do you swim?

Ned: I swim _____ in the pool every

day. My coach puts me through all my

_____ every day, too.

Tammy: Do you think you could give us a

_____?

Ned: Sure! Just watch!

Name _____

Long *i*

Write a word from the box to complete each sentence.

Word Bank

midnight	frightened	sightseeing	untie
dries	butterflies	lightning	supplies

1. Are both wings on _____ exactly

   the same?

2. I am always asleep at _____.

3. When we visited Toronto, we took a

   _____ bus.

4. Do you buy your art _____

   at the art store?

5. When I am scared, I am _____.

6. Who will help me _____ this bow?

7. Do you like thunder and _____ storms?

8. After dinner, I wash the dishes and my sister

   _____ them.

Name _____

Circus Action

Write the correct verb to complete each sentence.

1. Yesterday, Nora _____ me
   the circus was in town.

tell	told

2. Now Nora and Tron _____
   in their seats at the circus.

sit	sat

3. During the last act, one clown

   _____ up a balloon.

blow	blew

4. Now Nora and Tron _____
   up from their seats.

get	got

5. They _____ to the
   refreshment stand now.

go	went

6. A few minutes ago, two men

   _____ fresh popcorn.

make	made

7. Now Nora and Tron _____
   fifty cents to the men at the stand.

give	gave

8. A while ago, they _____
   the clowns eating popcorn, too.

see	saw

Spelling Review

Write Spelling Words from the list to answer the questions.

1–6. Which words have a vowel sound spelled oo?

1. _____   4. _____

2. _____   5. _____

3. _____   6. _____

7–15. Which words have the long i sound?

7. _____   12. _____

8. _____   13. _____

9. _____   14. _____

10. _____   15. _____

11. _____

16–22. Which words end with ed or ing?

16. _____   20. _____

17. _____   21. _____

18. _____   22. _____

19. _____

Spelling Words

1. named
2. high
3. zoo
4. moon
5. liked
6. good
7. night
8. mind
9. riding
10. took
11. sky
12. using
13. hoping
14. room
15. find
16. making
17. hook
18. light
19. chased
20. fly

Name _____

Details Chart

**Fill in the chart. Find two story details that tell
more about each sentence.**

Raymond's Best Summer
Raymond is upset about being asked to sit down while the others swim.   1. _____   _____   2. _____
Raymond is happy to show off his swimming skills.   3. _____   _____   4. _____
Lori is a good swimming teacher.   5. _____   _____   6. _____

Name _____

What Does It Mean?

**Read the different meanings for each word. Then write
a sentence for each meaning.**

desert

    a dry area where it doesn't rain often
    to go away from; to leave something behind

1. _____

2. _____

present

    a gift
    to give

3. _____

4. _____

fly

    move through the air
    an insect

5. _____

6. _____

Name _____

Spelling Spree

Short Cuts Add letters to each word to make a Spelling Word. Write it on the line.

Spelling Words

1. din _____

2. has _____

3. to _____

4. sing _____

5. go _____

Spelling Words

1. room
2. good
3. liked
4. took
5. riding
6. night
7. chased
8. light
9. hook
10. using

Rhyme Time Finish the sentences. Write the Spelling Word that rhymes with the word in dark print. Be sure each sentence makes sense!

6. The campers **hiked** as often as they _____.

7. Did you see the **book** beside that _____?

8. It is never **bright** in the dark of _____.

9. I saw a mouse **zoom** across the _____.

10. Do you think you **might** turn on the _____?

Name _____

Finding Adjectives

**Find and circle eight adjectives
in the sentences below.**

1. Sheila took a dive into deep water.

2. The strong swimmer swam two laps.

3. Five friends gave an enormous cheer.

**Write each adjective from above under the words that tell more
about it. Add new adjectives to the first two lists.**

What Kind?	How Many?	Special Adjectives
_____	_____	_____
_____	_____	_____
_____	_____	_____
_____	_____	_____
_____	_____	_____
_____	_____	_____

Name _____

Proofreading and Writing

Proofreading Circle four Spelling Words that are wrong in this talent show review. Then write each word correctly.

Spelling Words

1. named
2. moon
3. high
4. making
5. mind
6. fly
7. find
8. hoping
9. zoo
10. sky

At the talent show, one girl walked on hihg stilts. One boy's bird could fli with a flag in its beak! Another child could finde any city on a map. Two children were nameed the top winners.

1. _____   3. _____

2. _____   4. _____

Missing Letters Write the missing letters in the Spelling Words below.

5. m ___ ___ n   8. z ___ ___

6. s ___ y   9. m ___ ___ ing

7. hop ___ ___ ___   10. m ___ ___ d

Write a Description On another sheet of paper, write about a talent show act. Use Spelling Review Words.

Name _____

Test Practice

**Use the three steps you've learned to write a response to the
prompt below. Complete the chart, and then write your narrative
on the lines below it. Use the Revising Checklist on page 278 to
revise your paper.**

1. Think about a holiday. Write a personal narrative
   about one time your family celebrated this holiday.
   Include many details.

I will write about:	
What happened:	
Event:	Detail:
Event:	Detail:
Event:	Detail:

_____

_____

_____

_____

Continue on page 278.

Theme 6: **Talent Show**   277

Name _____

Test Practice continued

_____

_____

_____

_____

_____

_____

_____

_____

_____

_____

_____

Use another piece of paper if you need to.

Revising Checklist

✔ Does my paper fit the prompt?

✔ Does my paper tell about events in the order they happened?

✔ Can I add more details about each event?

✔ Have I used clear handwriting and corrected any mistakes?

**Read your story aloud to a partner. Then discuss your
answers to the questions on the Revising Checklist.
Make any changes that will make your paper better.**

Name _____

Riddle Time

Read each riddle. Write a word from the box to answer it.

Word Bank

station	newscast	bamboo	adventure
planet	insect	banjo	boomerang

1. I am another name for a bug.
   What am I?   _____

2. Trains arrive and leave from me.
   What am I?   _____

3. I am a musical instrument.
   What am I?   _____

4. You can find me in outer space.
   What am I?   _____

5. I am a stick that comes back to
   the person who throws me.
   What am I?   _____

6. I am a plant that pandas eat.
   What am I?   _____

7. You can watch me on television.
   I tell what is happening in the world.
   What am I?   _____

8. I am an exciting experience.
   What am I?   _____

Name _____

Solve This!

Read each paragraph and answer the questions.

Luis lost his baseball glove. He looks in his closet and in the garage, but he still can't find it. He remembers that his brother has a glove.

1. What is Luis's problem?

_____

_____

2. How does he try to solve his problem? _____

_____

3. How do you think Luis can solve his problem?

_____

Marta wants to play basketball. She asks Harry to play, but he wants to ride bikes. Marta starts shooting baskets alone, but she isn't having fun.

4. What is Marta's problem? _____

_____

5. How do you think Marta can solve her problem?

_____

_____

My Handbook

Contents

Penmanship Models

Trace and write the letters.

Aa Aa

Bb Bb

Cc Cc

Dd Dd

Ee Ee

Ff Ff

Gg Gg

Penmanship Models

Trace and write the letters.

Hh Hh

Ii Ii

Jj Jj

Kk Kk

Ll Ll

Mm Mm

Trace and write the letters.

Nn *Nn*

Oo *Oo*

Pp *Pp*

Qq *Qq*

Rr *Rr*

Ss *Ss*

Tt *Tt*

Penmanship Models

Trace and write the letters.

Uu Uu

Vv Vv

Ww Ww

Xx Xx

Yy Yy

Zz Zz

Trace and write the letters.

A a A a

B b B b

C c C c

D d D d

E e E e

F f F f

G g G g

Trace and write the letters.

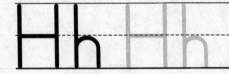 Hh Hh

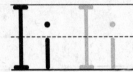 Ii Ii

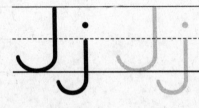 Jj Jj

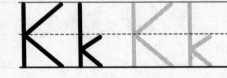 Kk Kk

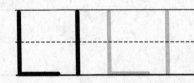 Ll Ll

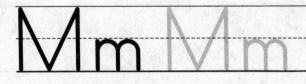 Mm Mm

Trace and write the letters.

Nn Nn

Oo Oo

Pp Pp

Qq Qq

Rr Rr

Ss Ss

Tt Tt

Trace and write the letters.

Uu Uu

Vv Vv

Ww Ww

Xx Xx

Yy Yy

Zz Zz

How to Study a Word

1. LOOK at the word.

➤ What does the word mean?

➤ What letters are in the word?

➤ Name and touch each letter.

2. SAY the word.

➤ Listen for the consonant sounds.

➤ Listen for the vowel sounds.

3. THINK about the word.

➤ How is each sound spelled?

➤ Close your eyes and picture the word.

➤ What other words have the same spelling patterns?

4. WRITE the word.

➤ Think about the sounds and the letters.

➤ Form the letters correctly.

5. CHECK the spelling.

➤ Did you spell the word the same way it is spelled in your word list?

➤ Write the word again if you did not spell it correctly.

A
about
again
a lot
always
am
and
any
are
around
as

B
back
because
been
before

C
cannot
caught
come
coming
could

D
do
does
done
down

E
enough

F
family
first
for
found
friend
from

G
getting
girl
goes
going

H
has
have
heard
her
here
his
how

I
I'd
if
I'll
I'm
into

it
it's

K
knew
know

L
letter
little

M
many
more
my
myself

N
name
never
new
now

O
of
off
on
once
one
other
our
outside

P
people
pretty

R
really
right

S
said
school
some
something
started
stopped

T
that's
the
their
there
they
thought
through
time
to
today
too

tried
two

V
very

W
want
was
went
were
what
when
where
who
will
would
write

Y
you
your

Take-Home Word List

Amazing Animals:
Reading-Writing Workshop

Look carefully at how these words are spelled.

Spelling Words

1. done
2. one
3. two
4. back
5. some
6. your
7. I'll
8. around
9. found
10. once
11. girl
12. into

Challenge Words

1. knew
2. pretty

My Study List
Add your own spelling words on the back. ➡

Take-Home Word List

Officer Buckle and Gloria

The Vowel + *r* Sound in *car*

vowel + **r** sound ➡ c**ar**, sm**ar**t

Spelling Words

1. car
2. smart
3. arm
4. park
5. yard
6. part
7. barn
8. hard
9. party
10. farm
11. are
12. warm

Challenge Words

1. department
2. carpet

My Study List
Add your own spelling words on the back. ➡

Take-Home Word List

Name_____

 My Study List

1. _____
2. _____
3. _____
4. _____
5. _____
6. _____
7. _____
8. _____
9. _____
10. _____

Review Words

1. start
2. far

How to Study a Word

Look at the word.
Say the word.
Think about the word.
Write the word.
Check the spelling.

294

Take-Home Word List

Name_____

 My Study List

1. _____
2. _____
3. _____
4. _____
5. _____
6. _____
7. _____
8. _____
9. _____
10. _____

How to Study a Word

Look at the word.
Say the word.
Think about the word.
Write the word.
Check the spelling.

294

Take-Home Word List

The Great Ball Game

More Long *o* Spellings

long **o** sound ➡ g**o**ld

b**oa**t

sl**ow**

Spelling Words

1. boat
2. cold
3. road
4. blow
5. gold
6. old
7. load
8. snow
9. hold
10. most
11. toe
12. do

Challenge Words

1. goal
2. rainbow

My Study List
Add your own spelling words on the back. ➡

295

Take-Home Word List

Ant

Words That End with *nd*, *ng*, or *nk*

nd ➡ ha**nd**

ng ➡ ki**ng**

nk ➡ tha**nk**

Spelling Words

1. king
2. thank
3. hand
4. sing
5. send
6. think
7. bring
8. bang
9. end
10. thing

Challenge Words

1. grand
2. young

My Study List
Add your own spelling words on the back. ➡

295

Take-Home Word List

Take-Home Word List

Name_____

My Study List

1._____

2._____

3._____

4._____

5._____

6._____

7._____

8._____

9._____

10._____

Review Words

1. and
2. long

How to Study a Word

Look at the word.
Say the word.
Think about the word.
Write the word.
Check the spelling.

Name_____

My Study List

1._____

2._____

3._____

4._____

5._____

6._____

7._____

8._____

9._____

10._____

Review Words

1. so
2. show

How to Study a Word

Look at the word.
Say the word.
Think about the word.
Write the word.
Check the spelling.

Take-Home Word List

Brothers and Sisters

Words That End with *er*

the vowel + **r** sound ➔ flow**er**

wat**er**

Spelling Words

1. flower
2. water
3. under
4. over
5. better
6. sister
7. brother
8. mother
9. father
10. after

Challenge Words

1. other
2. center

My Study List
Add your own spelling words on the back. ➔

Take-Home Word List

Amazing Animals:
Spelling Review

Spelling Words

1. farm
2. bring
3. hold
4. park
5. thing
6. boat
7. smart
8. sing
9. snow
10. yard
11. thank
12. blow
13. load
14. party
15. hand
16. most
17. cold
18. think
19. send
20. road

Challenge Words

1. department
2. grand
3. young
4. goal
5. rainbow

My Study List
Add your own spelling words on the back. ➔

Take-Home Word List

Name_____

My Study List

1. _____
2. _____
3. _____
4. _____
5. _____
6. _____
7. _____
8. _____
9. _____
10. _____

How to Study a Word
Look at the word.
Say the word.
Think about the word.
Write the word.
Check the spelling.

Take-Home Word List

Name_____

My Study List

1. _____
2. _____
3. _____
4. _____
5. _____
6. _____
7. _____
8. _____
9. _____
10. _____

Review Words

1. that
2. shop

How to Study a Word
Look at the word.
Say the word.
Think about the word.
Write the word.
Check the spelling.

Copyright © Houghton Mifflin Company. All rights reserved.

Take-Home Word List

Jalapeño Bagels

Contractions

A contraction is a short way of writing one or more words. An apostrophe replaces any dropped letters.

Spelling Words

1. I'll
2. we've
3. I'm
4. you're
5. isn't
6. didn't
7. you'll
8. I've
9. it's
10. we'll
11. can't

Challenge Words

1. they're
2. wouldn't

My Study List
Add your own spelling words on the back. ➡

Take-Home Word List

Family Time:
Reading-Writing Workshop

Look carefully at how these words are spelled.

Spelling Words

1. who
2. a lot
3. were
4. many
5. our
6. friend
7. cannot
8. here
9. first
10. today
11. would
12. could

Challenge Words

1. heard
2. again

My Study List
Add your own spelling words on the back. ➡

Take-Home Word List

Name _____

 My Study List

1. _____
2. _____
3. _____
4. _____
5. _____
6. _____
7. _____
8. _____
9. _____
10. _____

How to Study a Word

Look at the word.
Say the word.
Think about the word.
Write the word.
Check the spelling.

Take-Home Word List

Name _____

 My Study List

1. _____
2. _____
3. _____
4. _____
5. _____
6. _____
7. _____
8. _____
9. _____
10. _____

Review Words

1. it
2. us

How to Study a Word

Look at the word.
Say the word.
Think about the word.
Write the word.
Check the spelling.

Thunder Cake

Words That End with *-ed* or *-ing*
bat + t + ed ➡ bat**ted**
run + n + ing ➡ run**ning**

Spelling Words

1. batted
2. running
3. clapped
4. stopped
5. getting
6. shopping
7. stepped
8. hugging
9. pinned
10. sitting

Challenge Words

1. jogging
2. flipped

My Study List
Add your own spelling words on the back. ➡

Carousel

The Final Sound in *puppy*
puppy ➡ pup p**y**
baby ➡ ba b**y**

Spelling Words

1. puppy
2. baby
3. lucky
4. happy
5. very
6. lady
7. funny
8. silly
9. many
10. only
11. cookie

Challenge Words

1. furry
2. angry

My Study List
Add your own spelling words on the back. ➡

Take-Home Word List

Name_____

 My Study List

1. _____
2. _____
3. _____
4. _____
5. _____
6. _____
7. _____
8. _____
9. _____
10. _____

Review Words

1. me
2. bee

How to Study a Word

Look at the word.
Say the word.
Think about the word.
Write the word.
Check the spelling.

Take-Home Word List

Name_____

 My Study List

1. _____
2. _____
3. _____
4. _____
5. _____
6. _____
7. _____
8. _____
9. _____
10. _____

Review Words

1. this
2. must

How to Study a Word

Look at the word.
Say the word.
Think about the word.
Write the word.
Check the spelling.

Take-Home Word List

The Art Lesson

The Vowel Sounds in *moon* and *book*

moon → **zoo**, fo**o**d
book → h**oo**k, t**oo**k

Spelling Words

1. zoo
2. tooth
3. hook
4. moon
5. book
6. soon
7. took
8. good
9. room
10. foot
11. you
12. who

Challenge Words

1. hoof
2. school

My Study List
Add your own spelling words on the back. →

Take-Home Word List

Family Time:
Spelling Review

Spelling Words

1. better
2. isn't
3. happy
4. clapped
5. sister
6. I'll
7. lady
8. stopped
9. sitting
10. brother
11. I'm
12. baby
13. getting
14. mother
15. you're
16. puppy
17. hugging
18. I've
19. silly
20. it's

Challenge Words

1. other
2. they're
3. wouldn't
4. angry
5. jogging

My Study List
Add your own spelling words on the back. →

Take-Home Word List

Name_____

 My Study List

1. _____
2. _____
3. _____
4. _____
5. _____
6. _____
7. _____
8. _____
9. _____
10. _____

How to Study a Word

Look at the word.
Say the word.
Think about the word.
Write the word.
Check the spelling.

Take-Home Word List

Name_____

 My Study List

1. _____
2. _____
3. _____
4. _____
5. _____
6. _____
7. _____
8. _____
9. _____
10. _____

Review Words

1. too
2. cook

How to Study a Word

Look at the word.
Say the word.
Think about the word.
Write the word.
Check the spelling.

Take-Home Word List

Moses Goes to a Concert

More Long *i* Spellings

the long **i** sound → sk**y**, f**i**nd, n**igh**t

Spelling Words

1. sky
2. find
3. night
4. high
5. fly
6. try
7. light
8. dry
9. right
10. mind
11. eye
12. buy

Challenge Words

1. flight
2. reply

My Study List
Add your own spelling words on the back. →

Take-Home Word List

Talent Show: Reading-Writing Workshop

Look carefully at how these words are spelled.

Spelling Words

1. tried
2. never
3. going
4. coming
5. new
6. very
7. other
8. started
9. something
10. school
11. outside
12. people

Challenge Words

1. enough
2. through

My Study List
Add your own spelling words on the back. →

Take-Home Word List

Name_____

 My Study List

1. _____
2. _____
3. _____
4. _____
5. _____
6. _____
7. _____
8. _____
9. _____
10. _____

How to Study a Word

Look at the word.
Say the word.
Think about the word.
Write the word.
Check the spelling.

Take-Home Word List

Name_____

 My Study List

1. _____
2. _____
3. _____
4. _____
5. _____
6. _____
7. _____
8. _____
9. _____
10. _____

Review Words

1. why
2. my

How to Study a Word

Look at the word.
Say the word.
Think about the word.
Write the word.
Check the spelling.

Take-Home Word List

Talent Show:
Spelling Review

Spelling Words

1. took
2. fly
3. good
4. riding
5. high
6. room
7. night
8. find
9. chased
10. hoping
11. hook
12. mind
13. using
14. liked
15. making
16. zoo
17. light
18. named
19. sky
20. moon

Challenge Words

1. school
2. reply
3. flight
4. teasing
5. decided

My Study List
Add your own
spelling words
on the back. ➡

Take-Home Word List

The School Mural

More Words with *-ed* or *-ing*
like – e + ed ➡ lik**ed**
hope – e + ing ➡ hop**ing**

Spelling Words

1. liked
2. hoping
3. baked
4. using
5. chased
6. making
7. closed
8. hiding
9. named
10. riding

Challenge Words

1. teasing
2. decided

My Study List
Add your own
spelling words
on the back. ➡

Take-Home Word List

Name_____

 My Study List

1. _____
2. _____
3. _____
4. _____
5. _____
6. _____
7. _____
8. _____
9. _____
10. _____

Review Words

1. time
2. sleep

How to Study a Word

Look at the word.
Say the word.
Think about the word.
Write the word.
Check the spelling.

Take-Home Word List

Name_____

 My Study List

1. _____
2. _____
3. _____
4. _____
5. _____
6. _____
7. _____
8. _____
9. _____
10. _____

How to Study a Word

Look at the word.
Say the word.
Think about the word.
Write the word.
Check the spelling.

Take-Home Word List

Take-Home Word List

Focus on Chapter Books

Homophones are words that sound alike but have different spellings and meanings.
Example: **week** (7 days)
weak (not strong)

Spelling Words

1. tail
2. tale
3. plane
4. plain
5. sail
6. sale
7. to
8. too
9. two
10. hole
11. whole

Challenge Words

1. threw
2. through

My Study List
Add your own spelling words on the back. ➡

Focus on Biography

The Vowel + _r_ Sounds
vowel + **r** sound ➡ b**or**n, c**ore**

Spelling Words

1. born
2. core
3. short
4. morning
5. fork
6. four
7. horn
8. sport
9. torn
10. sort
11. snore
12. fort

Challenge Words

1. forty
2. forest

My Study List
Add your own spelling words on the back. ➡

Take-Home Word List

Name_____

 My Study List

1. _____
2. _____
3. _____
4. _____
5. _____
6. _____
7. _____
8. _____
9. _____
10. _____

Review Words

1. more
2. store

How to Study a Word

Look at the word.
Say the word.
Think about the word.
Write the word.
Check the spelling.

Take-Home Word List

Name_____

 My Study List

1. _____
2. _____
3. _____
4. _____
5. _____
6. _____
7. _____
8. _____
9. _____
10. _____

Review Words

1. for
2. four

How to Study a Word

Look at the word.
Say the word.
Think about the word.
Write the word.
Check the spelling.

Read each question. Check your paper for each kind of mistake. Correct any mistakes you find.

☐ Did I begin each sentence with a capital letter?

☐ Did I use the correct end mark?

☐ Did I spell each word correctly?

☐ Did I indent each paragraph?

Proofreading Marks		
∧	Add one or more words.	want to I see the play. ∧
——	Take out one or more words. Change the spelling.	The boat ~~did~~ moved slowly. filled The cloud ~~filed~~ the sky.
╱	Make a capital letter a small letter.	The A̸nimals hid from the storm.
≡	Make a small letter a capital letter.	There are thirty days in april.

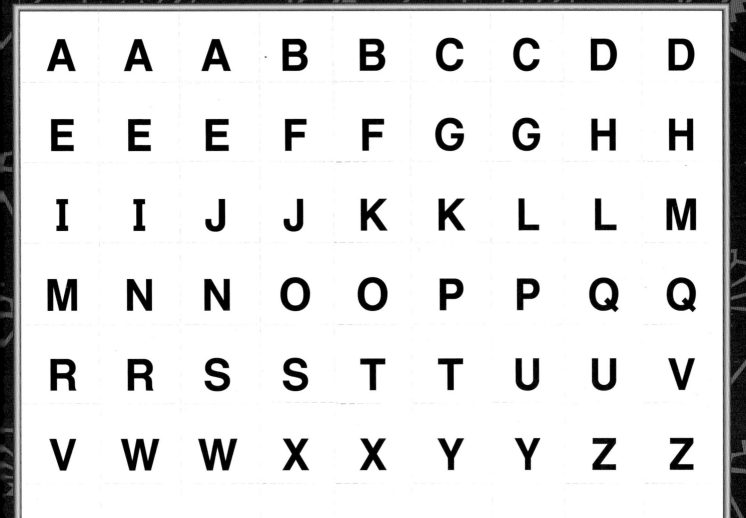

A	A	A	B	B	C	C	D	D
E	E	E	F	F	G	G	H	H
I	I	J	J	K	K	L	L	M
M	N	O	O	P	P	Q	Q
R	R	S	S	T	T	U	U	V
V	W	W	X	X	Y	Y	Z	Z

You can add punctuation marks or other letters to the blanks.

Letter Tray

Letter Tray

c a t

fold

fold

fold

d   d   c   c   b   b   a   a   a

h   h   g   g   f   f   e   e   e

m   l   l   k   k   j   j   i   i

q   q   p   p   o   o   n   n   m

v   u   u   t   t   s   s   r   r

z   z   y   y   x   x   w   w   v

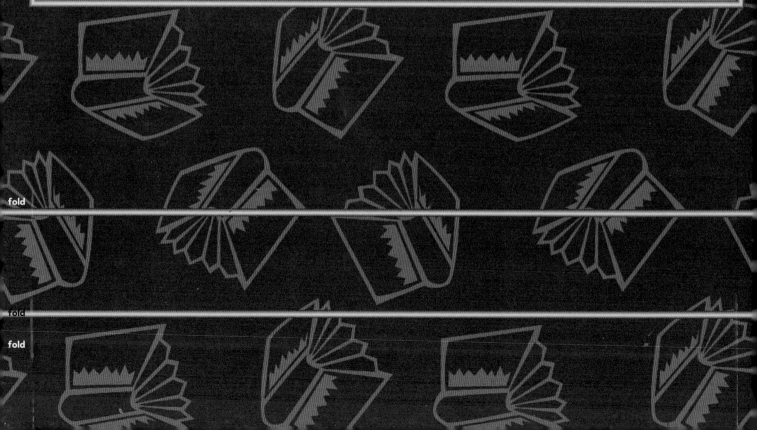

fold

fold

fold

	Moses Goes to a Concert	Thunder Cake
	alphabet	air
	heart	child
	mind	heavy
	The School Mural	hour
	below	The Art Lesson
	neighbor	fair
	should	gold
		woman

You can add your own words for sentence building.

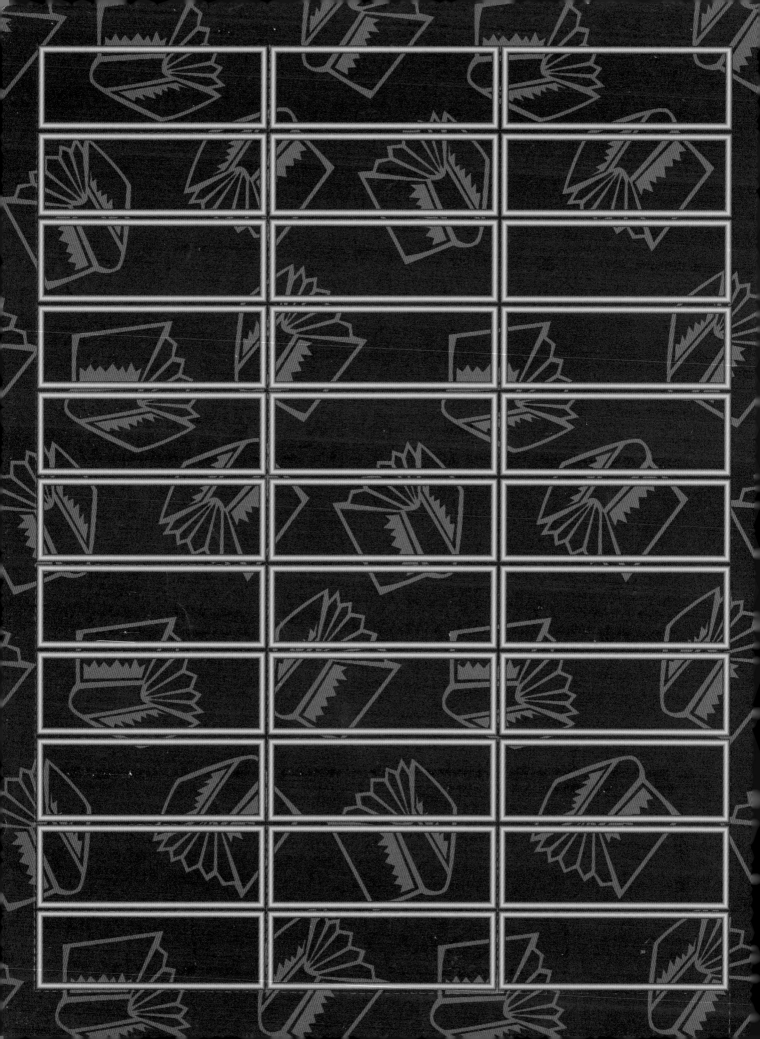

Theme 2, Week 3	Theme 2, Week 2	Theme 2, Week 1
Jalapeño Bagels	The Great Ball Game	Officer Buckle and Gloria
early	ago	board
hair	field	listen
instead	half	told
Carousel	Brothers & Sisters	Ant
aunt	middle	between
million	trouble	care
pair	uncle	weigh

You can add your own words for sentence building.

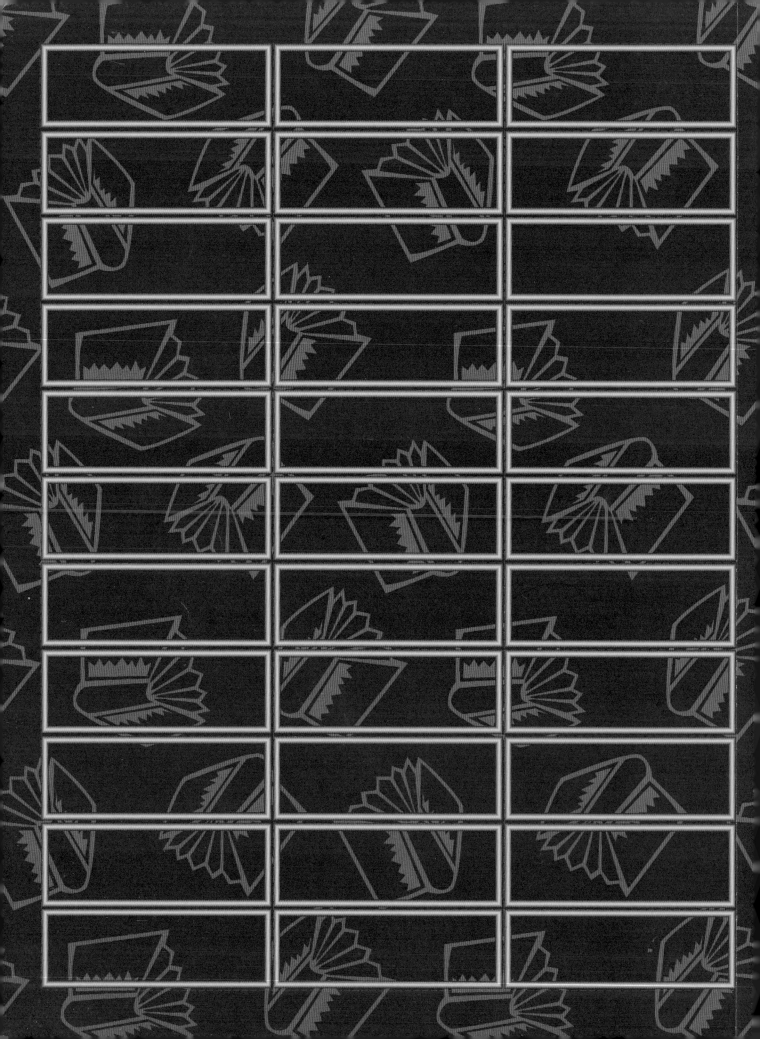